THE PHILLIPS COLLECTION

GIORGIONE (?)   The Hour Glass

This little panel for a piece of furniture is here attributed to the boyhood of Giorgione. It certainly reveals his liberating influence and his unique contribution to pictorial art. It could be called the earliest source of modern romantic landscape. The painted lyric which Giorgione invented is for the kindred spirits of artists and amateurs of every race and of any time. He was the first single-minded independent in the history of painting and was closer to the modern painters of romantic lyricism than to the masters of the High Renaissance.

D. P.

THE
PHILLIPS
COLLECTION

A MUSEUM OF MODERN ART

AND ITS SOURCES

CATALOGUE

WASHINGTON

PRODUCED BY
THAMES AND HUDSON NEW YORK AND LONDON
PRINTED AND BOUND IN GREAT BRITAIN BY
JARROLD AND SONS LTD. NORWICH 1952

THE Phillips Memorial Gallery was founded in 1918 in memory of my father, Major D. Clinch Phillips and my brother, James Laughlin Phillips. It was my thought that no mortuary monument remindful of the accident of death could suitably commemorate two such noble and vital men. To them and to my beloved mother Eliza Laughlin Phillips, this gallery and its cultural purpose are dedicated. The title however has been changed from the Phillips Memorial Gallery to the Phillips Collection. It is the diversity and unity of the Collection as a personal creation which gives to the Institution its purpose and meaning.

D. P.

INTRODUCTION

THIS is our first real catalogue. Although I have always realized the need for it, my awareness of the formative and malleable character of the Collection has influenced me to publish instead such books as A COLLECTION IN THE MAKING and THE ARTIST SEES DIFFERENTLY which expressed my point of view and philosophy but postponed the apparent decisions implied in any museum record and report. Incorporated in 1918 and active in loan exhibitions, publications, an art school (now discontinued), many lectures and more concerts during the thirty-two years under my Directorship—we have maintained our character as a privately endowed and subsidized and as an intimately personal institution. The Collection has been the creation of two artists who love painting very much, my wife Marjorie Phillips and myself. (It has been our wish to share our treasures with all open minded people.) They are welcomed to feel at home with the pictures in an unpretentious domestic setting which is at the same time physically restful and mentally stimulating. (We enjoy many ways of seeing and painting, none of which we claim to be the only right way.) This catalogue will reveal a catholicity of taste and a multiplicity of interests. (Yet we believe that there is a certain creative unity in all the variety,) such a unity as would be no less true of other private collections of comprehensive scope and personal taste devoted to the delightful duty of supporting and interpreting artists and relating them to each other in qualitative appreciations of their work. The Collection has grown and changed, but all within the severely limited space of the same old 1897 Washington house where the idea for it was born. Such a setting is of course inappropriate to a "museum of modern art and its sources" as our sub-title defines our character and it would never have been acceptable for so many years if financial depressions and world wars had not been thwarting circumstances. Our inability to draw upon public funds is the consequence of my will to maintain individuality of choice and independence of policy. Ours is a unique, unorthodox museum with a way of its own in not segregating periods and nationalities in order the better to show the universality of art and the continuities of such ancient seeing habits as realism, expressionism and constructivism. It was necessary to decide whether to build slowly and not buy or to buy freely and postpone building. The second alternative was inevitable because of our wish to exhibit and interpret a large and purposeful collection to the public during our own lives. The decision has been made easier because our friends from all over the world have seemed to like our many rearrangements and loan exhibitions in the same old fondly familiar place.

Our sub-title "A Museum of Modern Art and Its Sources" has never been accurately descriptive. We are not exclusively modern. In fact the first impression on entering is apt to be decidedly un-modern. It may well be argued that according to the usual meaning of the word we are not a museum at all. Our "sources" are not the often remote or ancient origins of current creations in the arts, which have not been within our scope since they would require space for large sculpture and for show-cases. All this is true. Nevertheless the contemporary works in our Collection far outnumber the works earlier than 1900. Consequently we are a museum of contemporary art and so also of modern art. Our sources of twentieth-century painting are great painters from the late fifteenth century up to the portals opening on today and tomorrow. Our modernists, in other words, our heroes of evolutionary progress in art, include Giorgione, El Greco, Chardin, Goya, Constable, Daumier, Delacroix, Corot, Courbet, Ryder, Manet, Renoir, Degas, Cézanne, Van Gogh, and Seurat, as well as Bonnard, Matisse, Rouault, Marin, Kokoschka, Klee, Picasso, Braque and Dove. Intensely interested as I am in all the functional forms and spatial intervals, the challenging self-sufficiencies and the stimulating shocks of art today, I only venture to say which of these I like well enough and consider sound, sincere and original enough to purchase and to exhibit as evidences of new life springing up from old roots, or of new discoveries out of our laboratory of trial and error—new devices and designs comparable to other modern products of research and technology. I do not venture to anticipate posterity and the ultimate valuations of history. It is impossible to judge contemporary works of art with historical detachment. The Collector can only be true to himself. My choices have been frankly personal and pervaded by only two predominant interests—the proved recurrence of the mightier trends in art and the assembling of related and contrasted personalities of past and present.

JEAN BAPTISTE SIMÉON CHARDIN

A Bowl of Plums

Acknowledging inability to present many interesting experimental works in the necessary space and light, and unwilling as well as unready to make an all-inclusive survey of every contemporary phase of painting, to show specimens of every conceptual and technical innovation, I am impelled to discriminate for and against. I select works which seem to add to my well-being by completing my satisfaction when the color is integrated with the line or form. For me an artist's unique personality must transcend any imposed pattern which otherwise becomes an academic stencil adaptable to mass production.

There are two opportunities of the intimate gallery which we cherish. (1) the collecting of groups of works early and late by favourite artists for exhibition units and (2) the chance to place well and to enjoy little masterpieces for small furnished rooms. An even more important privilege of the personal gallery is the stress which I can place on evolutionary developments of old technics and ways of seeing, avoiding period rooms and chronological arrangements, comparing many kinships which I have liked and leaving to other galleries personalities which are not for me.

To Henri Focillon I am indebted for the clearest statement on the transitional stages in the life of forms, the archaic and experimental times of ascent, the classic moments of serenity on a summit, the delectable refinements of the valleys and the new climb begun through the exploratory trails. Focillon also listed the most significant families of artists: the builders, the sensibilities, the mannerists, the virtuosi, and the visionaries. The two simplifications supplement each other, the first reminding us that civilizations have successions of prevailing trends in art, the second listing the most universal affinities of artists and reminding us that there are variations in every epoch, even in the ages of anonymity and imposed order, that differing and dissenting individuals conform only to their own sincerities and for spiritual comradeship seek their own kind across the ages.

Encouragement for the lone individualist is the hot spot of my endeavours in the world of art and that implies a wide and tolerant acceptance of a many-minded art for a many-minded world, with the reservation that I will buy and exhibit only what I can genuinely respect and enjoy.

A creative collection of paintings is conditioned and limited by circumstances, by the fate of favourite pictures too lovingly held or else obtainable only for prices too far beyond reach, and finally by the difficult choice when all but one of several simultaneous opportunities have to be renounced. It is often the destiny of a collector to remain dissatisfied with *any other* examples of an artist's work because of his frustration in obtaining *the one* picture which condenses that artist for him. The catalogue must now go to press with the collection still lacking a few paintings for which I have long waited and with many artists of past and present for whom I have genuine admiration still unrepresented.

In our unpretentious, disarmingly domestic and frankly undistinguished setting there are many obvious disadvantages and even dangers. But at least there is a sense of art lived with, worked with and loved. The audiences at our free concerts and lectures, and the throngs who attend our occasional loan exhibitions with their instructive labels and catalogues, are in marked contrast to the generally prevailing quiet of our galleries where there is an invitation to relax, to smoke, to think and enjoy. I believe I have used the word enjoy more than once in this preface and that is as it has to be if I am to introduce this Collection made with enjoyment for the enjoyment of others. As we move into a future menaced by evil forces of tyranny and total war we must cling to our faith in art as the symbol of the creative life and as the stronghold of the free and aspiring individual.

DUNCAN PHILLIPS

CATALOGUE OF THE PHILLIPS COLLECTION
AND ITS EXHIBITION UNITS

The asterisks after the names of a few of the artists, modern and contemporary, indicate that they are represented in the Collection by Exhibition Units. The paintings here selected for the catalogue, in conformity with its policy of listing a limited number of works by any painter, are at this time nominated for the Permanent Collection but might later be replaced or supplemented by other paintings of the Exhibition Units. From a great many of the other painters the Gallery has purchased more works than are listed in the catalogue.

PART I

ANDRÉ, ALBERT (French Contemporary)

THE CONCERT
wood panel 21×27, *signed* l.r.: Alb. André

HOUSE IN THE OLIVE TREES
canvas 18×21¾, *signed* l.l.: Alb. André

MELONS, PEPPERS AND GRAPES
canvas 17×21¾, *signed* l.r.: Albert André

ON THE BALCONY
canvas 32×25½, *signed* l.l.: Albert André

RENOIR IN HIS STUDIO AT CAGNES   *Plate 73*
canvas 20×26½, *signed* l.r.: Al. André, *painted* 1916

AVERY, MILTON (American Contemporary)*

BOTTLE AND MATCHES
oil on cardboard 16×22, *signed* l.r.: Milton Avery

GIRL WRITING
canvas 48×32, *signed* l.l.: Milton Avery

GLADIOLUS
canvas 26×34, *signed* l.l.: Milton Avery

GREEN LANDSCAPE
canvas 36×46, *signed* l.l.: Milton Avery

HARBOR AT NIGHT   *Plate 206b*
canvas 32×48, *signed* l.r.: Milton Avery

PINE CONES
canvas 28×36, *signed* l.l.: Milton Avery

3

SHELLS AND FISHERMEN
canvas 18×30, *signed* l.r.: Milton Avery

BEAL, GIFFORD (American Contemporary)*

CIRCUS PONIES   Plate 195b
wood panel 20×36, *signed* l.c.: Gifford Beal

THE GARDEN PARTY
canvas 18×24, *signed* l.c.: Gifford Beal 20

IMPRESSION FROM "LIFE WITH FATHER"   Plate 195a
masonite panel 8¼×20¼, *signed* l.l.: Gifford Beal
Exhibited: Tate Gallery, London, 1946, American Paintings Exhibition

ITALIAN FIESTA
gouache on blue paper 12×18, *unsigned*

PARADE OF ELEPHANTS
canvas 36×58½, *signed* twice, l.r.: Gifford Beal; l.l.: Gifford Beal 24

SCENE FROM "PARNELL"
composition panel 20×24, *signed* l.r.: Gifford Beal

SCENE FROM "DIE FLEDERMAUS"
plywood panel 20×24, *signed* l.r.: Gifford Beal

THE QUARRYMAN
canvas 18×24, *signed* l.r.: Gifford Beal

THE TERRACE
canvas 16×30, *signed* l.l.c.: Gifford Beal 22

BEAL, REYNOLDS (American Contemporary)

BEACH PONIES
canvas 26×36, *signed* l.l.: Reynolds Beal 1918

JACKSONVILLE WATERFRONT
canvas 24×30, *signed* l.r.: Reynolds Beal 1914

IN THE RIPS OFF MONTAUK
etching 9×12¾, *signed* on paper l.r.: Reynolds Beal 1928

OFF FOR THE GEORGES
etching 8¼×12¾, *signed* on paper l.r.: Reynolds Beal 1930

BELLOWS, GEORGE (American 1882–1925)

EMMA IN BLACK   Plate 166
canvas 40×33, *unsigned*
References: Peyton Boswell, Jr. "Bellows", p. 96

EDITH CAVELL
lithograph 18¾×24¾, drawn in 1918, *signed* in pencil l.r.: George Bellows;
Bellows catalogue no. 11

IRISH TOWN
lithograph 10¼×8⅛, drawn in 1923, *signed* on plate l.r.c.: Geo. Bellows,
on paper l.r.: Geo. Bellows; Bellows catalogue no. 7

MY FAMILY
lithograph 10 3/16×8, drawn in 1921, *signed* on plate l.r.: G.B.; on paper
in pencil: Geo. Bellows; Bellows catalogue no. 10

BERMAN, EUGENE (Russian-American Contemporary)

BRIDGE AT PADUA
ink and wash drawing 24×18, *signed* l.r.: E. Berman 1931

COURTYARD   Plate 219
canvas 36½×29, *signed* l.r.: E. Berman 1930

DAYBREAK   Plate 218
canvas 25½×21¼, *signed* l.r.: E. Berman 1930

NEAPOLITAN NIGHT
ink and wash drawing 17½×14¾, *signed* l.r.: E. Berman 1929

PARK AT ST. CLOUD
canvas 39½×32, *signed* l.l.: E. Berman 1932

BIDDLE, GEORGE (American Contemporary)

LANDSCAPE
canvas 12×18, *signed* l.l.: Biddle 1934

BLAKELOCK, RALPH ALBERT (American 1847–1919)

MOONLIGHT LANDSCAPE
wood panel $5\frac{3}{4}×9\frac{3}{4}$, *signed* l.r.: R. A. Blakelock

BLUEMNER, OSCAR (American 1867–1938)

ORANGES
watercolor $9\frac{1}{2}×12\frac{5}{8}$, *signed* l.l.: Bluemner

WAREHOUSE
gouache $9\frac{1}{2}×12\frac{1}{2}$, *painted* 1927, *signed* l.l.: Bluemner

BONNARD, PIERRE (French 1867–1947)*

CHILDREN AND CAT   Plate 107
canvas $22×27\frac{1}{2}$, *painted* 1910, *signed* l.c.: Bonnard
References: Leon Werth "Bonnard", pl. 7
Exhibited: Smith College Museum of Art, November–December 1932;
Bonnard-Vuillard Exhibition, Art Institute of Chicago, December
1938–January 1939; Bonnard-Vuillard Exhibition, Institute of Modern
Art, Boston, October 1944; Cincinnati Art Museum, 1951

CIRCUS RIDER (Le Cirque)   Plate 97
panel resembling masonite $10\frac{3}{4}×13\frac{3}{4}$, *signed* l.r.: Bonnard 94
Collections: Thadée Natanson, Paris; Dr. Soubies, Paris; Felix Fénéon,
Paris
References: Fénéon Collection sale catalogue, pl. 62; "Bijutsushinron",
1931, pl. 63; Album Druet, no. 10,169; Kenyon Review, Autumn 1949
illus. opp. p. 566
Exhibited: Galerie Durand Ruel, Paris, 1896; Galerie Druet, Paris, April
1924; Bolette Natanson, Paris, June 1936; Stedelijk Museum, Amsterdam
1939

THE CHEQUERED TABLE COVER   *Plate 109*
(loaned by Marjorie Phillips)
canvas 13¼×23⅞, *painted c.* 1924, *signed* l.r.: Bonnard
Collections: Henri Cannone, Paris
References: Duncan Phillips "Pierre Bonnard", Kenyon Review, Autumn
1949, p. 565, frontis.
Exhibited: Bonnard Exhibition, Cleveland Museum of Art, March–April
1948; Museum of Modern Art, May–July 1948

EARLY SPRING   *Plate 104*
canvas 34½×52, *signed* l.l.: Bonnard 1910
References: Duncan Phillips "Bonnard", Kenyon Review, Autumn 1949,
p. 564, illus.; Duncan Phillips "The Artist Sees Differently", vol. I,
p. 127, illus. vol. II, pl. 86
Exhibited: Century of Progress Exhibition, Art Institute of Chicago,
June–November 1933; Bonnard–Vuillard Exhibition, Art Institute of
Chicago, December 1938–January 1939, illus. in cat.; Virginia Museum
of Fine Arts, October–November 1950

GRAPE HARVEST   *Plate 111*
canvas 25×16, *painted c.* 1924, *signed* l.l.: Bonnard
Exhibited: Bonnard Exhibition, Smith College Museum of Art, Novem-
ber–December 1932; Museum of Modern Art, July–November 1933;
Lyman Allyn Museum, New London, March 1935; Buffalo Fine Arts
Academy, January 1936

INTERIOR WITH BOY
canvas 16×25, *painted* 1923, *signed* l.l.: Bonnard
Exhibited: Museum of Modern Art "Painting in Paris", January–February
1930; Art Institute of Chicago, Bonnard–Vuillard Exhibition, December
1938–January 1939; Institute of Modern Art, Boston, Bonnard–Vuillard
Exhibition, October–November 1944

THE LESSON   *Plate 108*
canvas 30×20, *painted c.* 1923, *signed* u.r.: Bonnard
Exhibited: Bonnard Exhibition, Smith College Museum of Art, November–December 1932

MOVEMENT OF THE STREET   *Plate 102*
canvas 14×19, *painted* 1900, *signed* l.l.c.: Bonnard
References: "Bonnard", Les Albums d'Art, Druet, illus.; John Rewald

"Bonnard", illus. p. 72; J. Meier-Graefe "Modern Painting", illus.; Daniel Catton Rich "Bonnard and Vuillard", foreword of cat., Art Institute of Chicago, 1938

Exhibited: Bonnard Exhibition, Smith College Museum of Art, November–December 1932; Bonnard-Vuillard Exhibition, Art Institute of Chicago, December 1938–January 1939; Bonnard-Vuillard Exhibition, Institute of Modern Art, Boston, October–November 1944; Bonnard Exhibition, Cleveland Museum of Art, March–April 1948; Museum of Modern Art, May–July 1948

NARROW STREET IN PARIS
composition panel $15\frac{1}{8} \times 8\frac{3}{8}$, *painted c.* 1904

THE OPEN WINDOW   Plate 113
canvas $46\frac{1}{2} \times 37\frac{3}{4}$, *painted* 1921, *signed* l.r.c.: Bonnard
References: Daniel Catton Rich "Bonnard and Vuillard", foreword of cat., Art Institute of Chicago, 1938; John Rewald "Bonnard", illus. p. 92; Kenyon Review, Autumn 1949, illus.; Leon Werth "Bonnard", pl. 37; Claude Roger-Marx "Peintres Français Nouveaux, no. 19—Bonnard", illus. p. 59; Rosamund Frost "Contemporary Art", p. 143
Exhibited: Museum of Modern Art, July–November 1933; Bonnard Exhibition, Art Institute of Chicago, December 1938–January 1939; Fogg Museum of Art, July–August 1941; Bonnard Exhibition, Cleveland Museum of Art, March–April 1948; Museum of Modern Art, May–July 1948

THE PALM   Plate 112
canvas $44 \times 57\frac{1}{2}$, *signed* l.r.: Bonnard 26
Collections: Félix Fénéon, Paris
References: The Arts, April 1928, p. 257, illus., note p. 253 by Forbes Watson; Creative Art, May 1929, color frontis.; Duncan Phillips "The Artist Sees Differently", vol. I, p. 127; vol. II, pl. 93; Smith College Museum of Art Bulletin, May 1933, illus. p. 17; Daniel Catton Rich "Bonnard and Vuillard", foreword of cat., Art Institute of Chicago, 1938; Sheldon Cheney "The Story of Modern Art" (1945), illus. p. 489; John Rewald "Bonnard" (1948), illus. p. 201
Exhibited: Cleveland Museum of Art, October 1929; Museum of Modern Art "Painting in Paris", January–February 1930; Smith College Museum of Art, Bonnard Exhibition, November–December 1932; Art Institute of Chicago, Century of Progress Exhibition, June–November 1933; Art

Institute of Chicago, Bonnard-Vuillard Exhibition, December 1938–
January 1939; Bonnard Exhibition, Cleveland Museum of Art, March,
April 1948; Museum of Modern Art, May–July 1948

PIAZZA DEL POPOLO
(loaned by Marjorie Phillips)
canvas $31\frac{1}{4} \times 38$, *signed* l.l.: Bonnard 1922

THE RIVIERA   Plate 110
canvas 31×30, *painted c.* 1923, *signed* l.r.: Bonnard
Collections: Claude Anet
References: Duncan Phillips "The Artist Sees Differently, vol. I, color
frontis.; vol. II, pl. 91; Daniel Catton Rich "Bonnard and Vuillard", Art
Institute of Chicago cat., 1938; John Rewald "Pierre Bonnard", illus. p. 93
Exhibited: Syracuse Museum of Fine Arts, 1930; Rochester Memorial Art
Gallery, 1930; Museum of Modern Art "Painting in Paris", January–
February 1930; Museum of Modern Art, July–November 1933; Phila-
delphia Museum of Art, January–February 1935; Yale University Art
Gallery, March 1936; Art Institute of Chicago, Bonnard-Vuillard
Exhibition, December 1938–January 1939; Golden Gate International
Exposition, San Francisco, May–October 1940; Bonnard Exhibition,
Cleveland Museum of Art, March–April 1948; Museum of Modern Art,
May–July, 1948

THE TERRACE   Plate 105
canvas 63×98, *signed* c.l.: Bonnard
References: Daniel Catton Rich "Bonnard and Vuillard", foreword of
cat. Art Institute of Chicago, 1938–9
Exhibited: Art Institute of Chicago, Bonnard-Vuillard Exhibition,
December 1938–January 1939

WOMAN AND DOG   Color Repr. and Plate 106
canvas $27 \times 15\frac{1}{2}$, *painted* 1922, *signed* u.r.: Bonnard
References: John Rewald "Bonnard", pl. 97
Exhibited: International Exhibition, Carnegie Institute, Pittsburgh, 1925;
Museum of Modern Art "Painting in Paris", January–February 1930;
Smith College Museum of Art, Bonnard Exhibition, November 1932;
Art Institute of Chicago, Bonnard-Vuillard Exhibition, December 1938–
January 1939; Bonnard Exhibition, Cleveland Museum of Art, March–
April 1948; Museum of Modern Art, May–July 1948

WOODS IN SUMMER
canvas 26×23, *painted c.* 1927, *signed* l.l.: Bonnard
Exhibited: Baltimore Museum of Art, 1928; Rochester Memorial Art Gallery, 1930; Smith College Museum of Art, Bonnard Exhibition, November 1932

FOUR BRUSH DRAWINGS
(illustrations for "Histoires Naturelles" by Jules Renard) 1904

And a group of lithographs

BOOTH, CAMERON (American Contemporary)

STREET IN STILLWATER   *Plate 232b*
tempera on paper 14¾×21, *painted c.* 1935, *signed* l.r.: Cameron Booth
Exhibited: Musée du Jeu de Paume, Paris, "Three Centuries of Art in the United States", 1938

BORIE, ADOLPHE (American 1877–1934)

THE FRENCH NOVEL
canvas 22×18, *signed* l.r.: Adolphe Borie

BOUCHÉ, LOUIS (American Contemporary)

END OF THE WORLD'S FAIR
canvas 20×24, *signed* l.l.: Louis Bouché 1941

BOUDIN, EUGÈNE LOUIS (French 1824–1898)

BEACH AT TROUVILLE   *Plate 38a*
wood panel 7×13¾, *signed* l.l.: E. Boudin 63 (?)
Exhibited: Art Institute of Chicago, Boudin Exhibition, 1935

BOURDELLE, ANTOINE (French 1861–1929)

VIRGIN OF ALSACE (La Vierge à L'Offrande)
marble 26 in. high, *signed* at base: Antoine Bourdelle 1920

BRADLEY, I. J. H. (American, active 1830–1855)

THE 'CELLIST   Plate 13
canvas 17¾×16, *signed* l.r.: I. Bradley Deli 1832
References: Jean Lipman "I. J. H. Bradley, Portrait Painter", Art in
America, July 1945, p. 154, illus. p. 157; Vergil Barker "History of
American Painting", illus. p. 3
Exhibited: Metropolitan Museum of Art, "Life in America", April–
October 1939, illus. p. 73 of cat., ref. p. 72; Baltimore Museum of Art,
May–September 1940; Tate Gallery, London, Exhibition of American
Painting, summer 1946; Detroit Institute of Arts, January 1948

BRAQUE, GEORGES (French Contemporary)*

STILL LIFE WITH GRAPES   Plate 177
canvas 21×29, *signed* l.r.: G. Braque 27
References: Jean Cassou "Georges Braque", Cahiers d'Art (no. 1, 1928),
illus. opp. p. 6; Henry R. Hope "Braque", pp. 106–07, illus, p. 106;
Rosamund Frost "Contemporary Art", p. 57; Sheldon Cheney "The
Story of Modern Art", illus. p. 463; Shoolman and Slatkin "The
Enjoyment of Art in America", pl. 577; Duncan Phillips, essay on
Braque and this painting for Twin Editions, Print No. 41
Exhibited: Museum of Modern Art "Painting in Paris", January–February
1930; Baltimore Museum of Art, January 1940; Braque Retrospective
Exhibition, Cleveland Museum of Art, January–March 1949; Museum
of Modern Art, March 30–June 1949; Massachusetts Institute of Tech-
nology, Braque Exhibition, March 1950

LEMONS AND NAPKIN RING   Plate 179c
canvas 16×47½, *signed* l.l.c.: G. Braque 28
References: E. Tériade "The Flowering of Braque's Art", Cahiers d'Art
(no. 10, 1928), illus. p. 365; Duncan Phillips "The Modern Argument
in Art and Its Answer", Bulletin of the Phillips Gallery 1931, p. 45,
illus. p. 46
Exhibited: Carnegie Institute, Pittsburgh, March 1936

LEMONS AND OYSTERS   Plate 178a
oval canvas 10¾×13¾, *painted* 1927, *signed* l.l.: G. Braque
Collections: Paul Rosenberg, Paris

LEMONS, PEACHES AND COMPOTIER   Plate *179b*
canvas 9 × 29, *signed* l.r.: G. Braque 27

PITCHER, PIPE AND PEAR   Plate *178b*
octagonal wood panel 13½ × 17, *signed* l.r.: G. Braque
Collections: Workman Collection, London
Exhibited: Museum of Modern Art, June–October 1930

PLUMS, PEARS, NUTS AND KNIFE   Plate *179a*
canvas 9 × 28¾, *signed* l.l.: G. Braque 26
Exhibited: Museum of Modern Art, January–March 1930

THE ROUND TABLE   Color *Repr. and Plate* 181
canvas 58 × 45, *signed* l.r.: G. Braque 29
Collections: Paul Rosenberg, Paris
References: E. Tériade "The Flowering of Braque's Art", Cahiers d'Art
(no. 10, 1928), illus. pp. 368–69; Art News, March 17, 1934, illus. on
cover, ref. p. 4; Alfred M. Frankfurter "Braque: the Compleat Decorator
on Exhibit", Art News, January 6, 1940, p. 10, ref. and illus.; Henry R.
Hope "Georges Braque", ref. p. 114, illus. p. 112
Exhibited: Durand-Ruel, New York, March 1934; Arts Club of Chicago,
Braque Retrospective, October–December 1939; San Francisco Museum
of Art, Braque Retrospective, January 1940; Braque Exhibition, Cleveland Museum of Art, January–March 1949; Museum of Modern Art,
March–June 1949

THE WASH STAND   Plate *180*
canvas 63⅞ × 25¼, *painted* 1944, *signed* l.l.: G. Braque
References: Cahiers d'Art 1940–44, p. 100, illus.; Stanislas Fumet
"Braque", pl. 23 in color; Aline Loucheim "ABC (or XYZ) of Abstract
Art", New York Times, Magazine Section, July 11, 1948, p. 42, illus.
Exhibited: Victoria and Albert Museum, London, 1946; Paul Rosenberg,
New York "21 Masterpieces by 7 Great Masters", November–December
1948, illus. in cat.

BREININ, RAYMOND (American Contemporary)

THE MAESTRO
canvas 32 × 40, *signed* l.l.: Breinin 40

BRUCE, EDWARD (American 1879–1943)

HUISSEAU SUR COSSON
canvas 17¼×22, *painted c.* 1926, *signed* l.l.: Edward Bruce

BURCHFIELD, CHARLES (American Contemporary)*

BARN   Plate 212a
watercolor 13¼×19¼, *signed* l.r.: Charles Burchfield 1917

CABIN IN NOON SUNLIGHT
watercolor 18×12, *signed* l.r.: Charles Burchfield 1925

MOONLIGHT OVER THE ARBOR
watercolor 19¼×13½, *signed*: Charles Burchfield 1916

OHIO RIVER SHANTY
watercolor 21×30, *signed* l.r.: Chas. Burchfield 1930

RAINY NIGHT
watercolor 18×12, *signed* l.l.: C. Burchfield 1918

ROAD AND SKY
watercolor 17½×21½, *signed* l.r.: Chas. Burchfield 1917

SULTRY AFTERNOON
watercolor 28¾×22½, *signed* l.r.: C E B 1944

THREE DAYS OF RAIN   Plate 213
watercolor 26½×14¼, *painted c.* 1918, *unsigned*

WOMAN IN DOORWAY   Plate 212b
tempera on mounted cloth 24×30, *signed* l.r.: C. Burchfield 1917
References: C. Law Watkins "The Language of Design", illus. p. 38
Exhibited: Carnegie Institute, Pittsburgh, Burchfield Exhibition, March
1938; Syracuse Museum, March–April 1939

BURLIUK, DAVID (Russian-American Contemporary)*

AT THE INN   Plate 171
canvas 14×18, *painted* 1936, *unsigned*

FLOWERS IN BLUE PITCHER
canvas 18 × 13, *signed* l.l.: Burliuk

A SEA-GOING STREET
watercolor 10 × 15, *signed* l.r.: Burliuk 1927

ON THE ROAD
canvas 33¼ × 48, *signed* l.l.: Burliuk

THE RAINBOW
canvas 17¼ × 24¼, *signed* l.l.: Burliuk

SHELLS
canvas 16 × 20, *signed* l.l.: Burliuk 1930

SHELLS AND PLANT
canvas 16 × 20, *signed* l.r.: Burliuk 32
References: Katherine Dreier "Burliuk", foreword by Duncan Phillips, illus.

SLOPES OF BEAR MOUNTAIN
canvas 18 × 13, *signed* l.r.: Burliuk 1925

CALLAHAN, KENNETH (American Contemporary)

JOURNEY ON A STAR
composition panel 20 × 30, *painted* 1947, *unsigned*

CANADÉ, VINCENT (American Contemporary)

TOWN BY A RIVER
canvas 30 × 24, *signed* l.r.: Vincent Canadé

CARPEAUX, JEAN BAPTISTE (French 1827–1875)

STREET SCENE   *Plate 29*
canvas 18 × 15, *unsigned*
References: Duncan Phillips "The Artist Sees Differently", vol. 1, pp. 110–11, illus.

14

CÉZANNE, PAUL (French 1839–1906)*

FIELDS AT BELLEVUE   Plate 66
canvas 14¼ × 19¾, *painted 1885–87, unsigned*
Collections: Egisto Fabbri, Florence
References: Lionello Venturi "Cézanne", no. 449, illus. pl. 131; Enciclo-
pedia Italiana, tome IX, colorplate; Dedalo, 1920, p. 69; L'Amour de
L'Art, November 1924, p. 343
Exhibited: 12th International Exhibition, Venice, Cézanne Hall, no. 21;
Museum of Historic Art, Princeton, November–December 1941

HARVESTERS (Les Moissonneurs)   Plate 67
canvas 10 × 16, *painted 1875–78, unsigned*
Collections: Ambroise Vollard, Paris; John Osborne Sumner, Boston
References: L. Venturi "Cézanne", no. 1517, pl. 386
Exhibited: Akron Art Institute, September 1947

MTE. STE. VICTOIRE (La Montagne Sainte Victoire au Grand Pin)   Plate 69
canvas 23½ × 28½, *painted 1885–87, unsigned*
Collections: Dr. J. F. Reber, Lausanne; Paul Rosenberg, Paris
References: Meier-Graefe "Cézanne und sein Kreis" (1922), p. 177;
"Entwicklungsgeschichte", pl. 500; Joachim Gasquet "Cézanne" (1926),
illus.; Kurt Pfister "Cézanne, Gestalt-Werk-Mytos" (1927), pl. 42;
Formes, November 1930; Duncan Phillips "A Classic Cézanne",
Bulletin of The Phillips Gallery (1931), pp. 9–11, illus. p. 8; L'Arte,
March 1935, p. 145, pl. 15; John Rewald "Paul Cézanne" (1939), p. 139,
pl. 82; Bernard Dorival "Cézanne", p. 52, pl. 87; Shoolman and
Slatkin "The Enjoyment of Art in America" (1942), p. 560, pl. 567;
C. Law Watkins "The Language of Design" (1946), p. 167, illus.
p. 166; John Rewald "The History of Impressionism" (1946), illus. p.
378; Fiske Kimball and Lionello Venturi "Great Paintings in America"
(1948), ref. and illus. in color, p. 194
Exhibited: Durand-Ruel, New York, Cézanne Exhibition, 1938;
Museum of Modern Art "Modern Masters", 1940, illus. p. 18; Art
Gallery of Toronto, February 1944; Yale University Art Gallery,
Cézanne Exhibition, January–February 1945; Brooklyn Museum
"Landscape", October 1945; Wildenstein, New York, Cézanne Exhi-
bition, 1947; Minneapolis Institute of Fine Arts, Cézanne Exhibition,
January 1950

POMEGRANATE AND PEARS *(Vase Paillé et Fruits sur une Table)* **Plate 70**
(Gift of Gifford Phillips, in memory of his father, James Laughlin Phillips)
canvas 18¼×21⅞, *painted 1895–1900, unsigned*
Collections: Claude Monet, Giverny; Joseph Stransky, New York
References: L. Venturi "Cezanne", no. 733, pl. 242; Art News, May 16, 1931, illus. in color, p. 99; René Huyghe "Cézanne et son Oeuvre", L'Amour de L'Art, May 1936, p. 178, fig. 64
Exhibited: Museum of Modern Art, First Loan Exhibition, 1929, illus. in cat.; Worcester Art Museum, 1932; Philadelphia Museum of Art, Cézanne Exhibition, 1934; Musée de l'Orangerie, Cézanne Exhibition, Paris 1936

SEATED WOMAN IN BLUE (La Dame au Livre) **Color Repr. and Plate 71**
canvas 26×19⅝, *painted c. 1900–04, unsigned*
Collections: Ambroise Vollard, Paris
References: L. Venturi "Cézanne", no. 703, pl. 230
Exhibited: Wildenstein Gallery, London, 1939

SELF PORTRAIT **Plate 68**
canvas 24×18½, *painted c. 1877, unsigned*
Collections: Ambroise Vollard, Paris; Theodor Behrens, Hamburg; J. Meier-Graefe, Berlin; Paul Cassirer, Berlin; Leo von Koenig, Schlach-tensee; Paul Rosenberg, Paris
References: Vollard "Paul Cézanne" (1914), pl. 45; Meier-Graefe "Cézanne und sein Kreis" (1922), p. 44, illus. p. 138; Meier-Graefe "Entwicklungsgeschichte", pl. 494; Meier-Graefe "Cézanne", frontis.; E. Waldmann "Die Kunst des Realismus und des Impressionismus", p. 495; Kurt Pfister "Cézanne, Gestalt-Werk-Mytos" (1927), pl. 42; Duncan Phillips "The Artist Sees Differently", vol. I, pp. 121–22, vol. II, pl. 55; Creative Art, May 1929, illus, p. 15; Art News, March 23, 1940, illus. p. 8; John Rewald "Paul Cézanne" (1939), pl. 62
Exhibited: Salon d'Automne, Paris, 1904, salle Paul Cézanne; St. Peters-burg, Russia, Exhibition of French Art, 1912; Paul Cassirer, Berlin, 1921, "Cézanne", illus. in cat. p. 5; Vienna, 82nd Exhibition of the Secession, 1925; Museum of Modern Art, First Loan Exhibition, November 1929, illus. in cat.; Museum of Modern Art, October 1930; Metropolitan Museum of Art, June–October 1932; Albright Gallery, Buffalo, October–November 1932; Philadelphia Museum of Art,

Cézanne Exhibition, November 1934, illus. in cat.; Golden Gate International Exposition, San Francisco, 1940, illus. in cat., p. 80; Durand-Ruel, New York "The 4 Great Impressionists", March 1940, illus. in cat.

CHAGALL, MARC (Russian-American Contemporary, School of Paris)

THE DREAM   *Plate 170*
gouache and pastel 20×26, *painted* 1939, *signed* l.r.: Marc Chagall

CHAPIN, JAMES (American Contemporary)

EMMETT MARVIN, FARMER
canvas 35×29, *signed* u.l.: James Chapin 25

ROAD
watercolor 10$\frac{1}{4}$×13$\frac{1}{4}$, *signed* l.l.: James Chapin 24

CHARDIN, JEAN BAPTISTE SIMÉON (French 1699–1779)

A BOWL OF PLUMS   *Color Repr. and Plate 7*
canvas 17$\frac{3}{4}$×22$\frac{1}{2}$, *unsigned*
Collections: Roberts Collection, London
References: Catalogue raisonné no. 854, pl. 112; Duncan Phillips "A Collection in the Making", pl. 2; Duncan Phillips "The Artist Sees Differently", vol. I, p. 20; vol. II, pl. 3; Duncan Phillips "Personality in Art", Magazine of Art, April 1935, p. 219, illus.; Duncan Phillips, essay on Chardin and this painting for Twin Editions, Print No. 40

CHASE, WILLIAM M. (American 1849–1916)

HIDE AND SEEK   *Plate 52*
canvas 27$\frac{1}{2}$×36, *painted* 1888, *signed* l.r.: Wm. M. Chase
Collections: James S. Inglis, New York; Miss Elizabeth Inglis
References: Katharine Metcalf Roof "The Life and Art of William Merritt Chase" (1917), pp. 278–79, illus.; Art Digest, November 15, 1939, p. 8, illus.

Exhibited: Detroit Institute of Arts, 1916; Toledo Museum of Arts, 1916; Metropolitan Museum of Art, 1917; Art Institute of Chicago, 1939–40, illus. in cat.; American British Art Center, New York, 1948; John Herron Art Museum, Indianapolis, 1949

CHIRICO, GIORGIO DE (Italian Contemporary, School of Paris)

TWO HORSES
canvas 20×25½, *signed* u.r.: G. de Chirico

CIARDI, EMMA (Italian Contemporary)

SYMPHONY IN BLUE
canvas 18×36, *signed* l.r.: Emma Ciardi 1922

CLAIRIN, PIERRE EUGÈNE (French Contemporary)

BOAT LANDING
canvas 19×21¾, *signed* l.l.: Pierre Eugène Clairin

A CHÂTEAU   *Plate 207a*
canvas 15×21, *signed* l.l.: Pierre Eugène Clairin

COLEMAN, GLENN (American 1887–1932)

THE MEWS
canvas 25×30, *painted* 1926, *signed* l.r.: Coleman

MINETTA LANE
lithograph 11⅛×11, *signed* in pencil l.l.; 1928 Glenn O. Coleman

CONSTABLE, JOHN (English 1776–1837)

ENGLISH LANDSCAPE   *Plate 10b*
wood panel 9½×12½, *unsigned*

ON THE RIVER STOUR   *Plate 11*
canvas 24×31, *unsigned*
Collections: Sir Joseph Beecham
Exhibited: Fogg Museum of Art, 1930; Fogg Museum of Art, 1940; Wildenstein, New York "The French Revolution", December 1943; Museum of Fine Arts, Boston "Works of Turner, Constable and Bonington", March 1949

COROT, JEAN BAPTISTE CAMILLE (French 1796–1875)

CIVITA CASTELLANA, PLAINS AND MOUNTAINS   *Plate 15b*
oil on paper mounted on canvas $8\frac{5}{8} \times 13\frac{7}{8}$, *painted* 1826–27, *unsigned*
Collections: Rousset, Paris
References: Robaut, vol. II, no. 142; vol. III, p. 53; vol. IV, p. 226; Vente Corot, Paris, 1875, no. 271

DAIRY FARM (La Grande Métairie, Ville d'Avray)   *Plate 33*
canvas $22 \times 31\frac{1}{2}$, *painted* 1860–65, *signed* l.l.: Corot
Collections: Laurent Richard Dollfus, Paris; Harold Somers, Brooklyn
References: Robaut, no. 1694, pl. 168
Exhibited: Museum of Modern Art, "Corot, Daumier", October–November 1930; New York World's Fair "Masterpieces of Art", May–October 1940; National Gallery of Art, Washington, 1941

PORTRAIT OF A WOMAN   *Plate 32*
canvas $15\frac{1}{2} \times 12\frac{3}{4}$, *painted* 1865–70, *signed* u.l.: Corot
Collections: Dikran Kélékian, Paris, New York
References: Robaut, no. 1390, vol. III, illus.; Arsène Alexandre "Sur la Collection Kélékian", Kélékian Collection Cat., p. 9, pl. 10
Exhibited: Philadelphia Museum of Art, Corot Exhibition, May–June 1946

VIEW FROM THE FARNESE GARDENS, ROME   *Plate 15a*
canvas $9\frac{1}{2} \times 15\frac{3}{4}$, *unsigned, dated* l.r.: Mars 1826
Collections: Détrimont, Paris; Quincy Adams Shaw; Mrs. Malcolm Graeme Haughton
References: Robaut, no. 65; Vente Corot, no. 17
Exhibited: Fogg Museum of Art, March–April 1929; Philadelphia Museum of Art, Corot Exhibition, May–June 1946; Art Gallery of Toronto, Corot Exhibition, January–February 1950

COURBET, GUSTAVE (French 1819–1877)

THE MEDITERRANEAN *Plate 34*
canvas 23 × 33, *painted c.* 1854–60, *signed* l.l.: Courbet
Collections: Burton Mansfield
Exhibited: Centenary Exh. of Courbet, Metropolitan Museum of Art, 1919; Marie Harriman Gallery, "Courbet and Delacroix", 1933; Baltimore Museum of Art, Courbet Exh., May 1938; Marie Harriman Gallery, Courbet Exh., November 1940; Arts Club of Chicago, Courbet Exh., January 1941; Wildenstein, New York "Courbet", December 1948

ROCKS AT ORNANS *Plate 35*
canvas 30 × 46, *painted c.* 1850, *signed* l.l.: G. Courbet
Collections: de Rochecouste; Georges Petit, Paris
References: Leonce Benedite "Courbet", p. 45; Creative Art, May 1929, illus. p. 18; Frank Jewett Mather "Modern Painting", illus. p. 170
Exhibited: Cleveland Museum of Art "French Art Since 1800", 1929; National Gallery of Art, Washington, June–October 1941; Wildenstein, New York "Courbet", illus. in cat., December 1948; Currier Gallery of Art, Manchester N. H. "Monet and the Beginnings of Impressionism", October 1949, illus. in cat.

CROCE, GIROLAMO DA SANTA (Italian *c.* 1503–1556)

LANDSCAPE WITH RIDER
wood panel 10½ × 19, *unsigned*

DAUMIER, HONORÉ (French 1808–1879)*

FOR THE DEFENSE (Le Défenseur) *Plate 24*
ink wash drawing 9 × 14, *signed* l.l.: h.d.
Collections: Alexis Rouart; Henri Rouart
References: Fuchs "Der Maler Daumier", p. 54, no. 196c, illus.; Martine and Marotte "Dessins de Maîtres Français", vol. IV, no. 24; R. Escholier "Daumier, peintre et lithographe", 1923, illus. opp. p. 108; Fleischmann "Daumier", illus. p. 26; Ars Graphica, pl. 25
Exhibited: École des Beaux-Arts, Paris, 1901 "Exposition Daumier";

"Exposition Daumier-Gavarni", 1923; Galerie Dru "Aquarelles et Dessins de Daumier", 1927; Musée de l'Orangerie, "Exposition Daumier" 1934, no. 132; American-British Art Center, New York "19th & 20th Century Drawings", January 1944; California Palace of the Legion of Honor "19th Century French Drawings", March 1947

ON A BRIDGE AT NIGHT (Femme et Enfant sur un Pont)   Plate 20
wood panel 10½ × 8½, *unsigned*
Collections: Arsène Alexandre; Alphonse Kann; Dikran Kélékian
References: Collection Kélékian, no. 26, illus.; Fuchs "Der Maler Daumier", pl. 68*a*
Exhibited: Museum of Modern Art "Corot-Daumier", 1930

THE PAINTER AT HIS EASEL (Le Peintre devant son Tableau)   Plate 23
(loaned by Marjorie Phillips)
wood panel 13⅛ × 10¼, *signed* l.l.: h.d.
Collections: Dollfus, Paris; Rosenberg, Paris; Jules Straus, Paris; E. Bignou, Paris; Sir William Burrell, Glasgow; Cargill, Scotland
References: A. Alexandre "Daumier-L'Homme et Son Oeuvre" (1888), p. 374; G. Geffroy "Les Artistes de Tous les Temps: Daumier" (*c.* 1901), p. 18, illus.; E. Klossowski "Daumier", 1908, no. 391, pl. 77; 1923 edition, pl. 145; Léon Rosenthal "L'Art de Notre Temps: Daumier" (1911), pp. 109–10, illus. p. 110; R. Escholier "L'Art et la Vie Romantiques: Daumier" (1923), illus. p. 121; R. Escholier "Daumier" (1930), pl. 46; Michael Sadler "Daumier, the Man and the Artist" (1924), pl. 61; E. Fuchs "Der Maler Daumier", no. 273, ref. and illus.; Giovanni Scheiwiller "Daumier" (1936), pl. 1; Jacques Lassaigne "Daumier" (1938), illus. p. 55; P. G. Konody and the Countess of Lathom "An Introduction to French Painting" (1932), illus. p. 178; The Studio, London, 1929; Studio Publications, New York, 1934, "The World's Masters: Honoré Daumier", pl. 1; Apollo, London, July 1929, illus.; The Bulletin, London, April 30, 1927, illus.; Drawing and Design, London, December 1927, illus.
Exhibited: Paris, 1878 "Exposition d'oeuvres de Daumier; École des Beaux-Arts, Paris, 1901, "Exposition Daumier"; Glasgow, May 1927 "A Century of French Painting", illus. in cat.; Reid and Lefèvre, London, November 1927 "Paintings and Drawings by Honoré Daumier", illus. in cat.; Bignou Gallery, New York, November 1940, "French Painters of the Romantic Period"

THE STRONG MAN *(Hercule de Foire)* *Plate 22*
wood panel 10½ × 13¾, *signed* l.l.: h. Daumier
Collections: A. Reid, Glasgow; Victor Desfossés, Paris; Baron Vitta, Paris
References: A. Alexandre "Daumier" (1888), p. 375; E. Klossowski "Daumier" (1923), no. 184, pl. 85; E. Fuchs "Der Maler Daumier" (1927), no. 125, p. 50; Art and Understanding, November 1929, frontis. and ref.
Exhibited: Kansas City Art Institute, 1931; M. H. De Young Museum, San Francisco "7 Centuries of Painting", January 1940

THREE LAWYERS *(Trois Avocats)* *Plate 25*
canvas 16 × 13, *signed* l.l.: h. Daumier
Collections: Henri Rouart, Paris; George Blumenthal, New York
References: E. Klossowski "Daumier" (1923), no. 122, pl. 70; Fuchs "Der Maler Daumier", p. 46, pl. 23; Escholier "Daumier" (1930), pl. 42; Jacques Lassaigne "Daumier" (1938), pl. 74; International Studio, September 1929, illus. p. 22
Exhibited: Exposition Centennale, 1889, no. 233; Museum of Modern Art, "Corot-Daumier", 1930, illus. in cat.; Musée du Louvre, Paris, Daumier Exh., 1934; Museum of Fine Arts, Boston, 1935; Golden Gate International Exposition, San Francisco, 1940, no. 257, illus. in cat.

TO THE STREET *(La Rue)* *Plate 21*
wood panel 10¾ × 8½, *unsigned*
Collections: M. A. D. Geoffroy, Paris; E. Bignou, Paris; Alex. Reid, Glasgow; Cargill, Scotland
References: E. Fuchs "Der Maler Daumier" (1927 & 1930), no. 60, ref. and illus.; Maurice Sachs "Honoré Daumier", p. 24, illus. p. 70; R. Escholier "Daumier" (1934), illus. p. 73; Art Digest, March 1944, illus. p. 7
Exhibited: Durand-Ruel, Paris, Daumier Exh., 1878, no. 78 in cat.; École des Beaux-Arts, Paris, 1901, Daumier Exh., cat. no. 44; Reid and Lefèvre, London, 1927, Daumier Exh.; Bignou Gallery, New York "French Painters of the Romantic Period", November 1940; University of North Carolina "From Ingres to Picasso", May 1941

TWO SCULPTORS *(L'Atelier du Sculpteur)* *Color Repr. and Plate 27*
wood panel 11 × 14, *unsigned*
Collections: Uhle, Dresden
References: Klossowski "Daumier", no. 381, pl. 142; Fuchs "Der Maler Daumier", p. 49, no. 96, pl. 96; Christian Zervos "Revisions Honoré

Daumier", Cahiers d'Art (no. 5–6, 1928), illus. p. 181; Lassaigne "Daumier" (1938), no. 48, illus.; Magazine of Art, February 1935, p. 83, illus., with note by Duncan Phillips
Exhibited: Museum of Modern Art, "Corot-Daumier", 1930, no. 87, illus. in cat.; Musée de l'Orangerie, Paris, 1934, Daumier Exh., no. 26; Yale University Art Gallery, 1936; Denver Art Museum, 1948, Daumier Exh.

THE UPRISING (L'Emeute)   *Plate 26*
canvas $24\frac{1}{2} \times 44\frac{1}{2}$, *painted c.* 1860?, *unsigned*
Rediscovered in 1924
Collections: Henry Bing, Paris
References: Arsène Alexandre "An Unpublished Daumier", Burlington Magazine, March 1924, pp. 143–4, illus. opp. p. 144; Michael Sadler "Daumier" (1924), pl. 53; E. Fuchs "Der Maler Daumier" (1927), pl. 9; Frank Jewett Mather "Modern Painting" (1927), p. 81, illus. p. 80; Frank Jewett Mather, The Arts, February 1927, pp. 77–78, illus.; Duncan Phillips "Daumier", Art and Understanding, November 1929, p. 46, frontis.; Duncan Phillips "A Collection Still in the Making", Creative Art, May 1929, p. 21, illus. p. 14; Meier-Graefe "Honoré Daumier, Fifty Years After", International Studio, September 1929, p. 25, illus. p. 24; Formes, November 1930, illus. p. 9; Hans Tietze "Masterpieces of European Art in American Collections", pl. 270; Sheldon Cheney "The Story of Modern Art" (1941), p. 113, illus. p. 99; Gazette des Beaux-Arts, July–December 1944, illus. p. 33 with quotation from Foçillon; Henri Foçillon "Visionnaires-Balzac et Daumier" from "Essays in Honor of Albert Feuillerat" (Yale University Press, 1943), pp. 201–02; C. Law Watkins "The Language of Design" (1946), p. 87, illus. p. 86; Duncan Phillips, Essay on Daumier and this painting for Twin Editions, Print No. 1
Exhibited: Musée du Louvre, 1924; Leicester Galleries, London, 1924; Reinhardt Gallery, New York, 1927; Museum of Modern Art, Corot-Daumier Exh., 1930, no. 61, illus.; Art Institute of Chicago, Century of Progress Exh., 1933, no. 242, illus.; Cleveland Museum of Art, Great Lakes Exh., 1936, no. 266; Toledo Museum of Art, November–December 1946, and Art Gallery of Toronto, January–February 1947 "The Spirit of Modern France", no. 27, illus. in cat.; City Art Museum, St. Louis "40 Masterpieces", 40th Anniv. Exh., October–November 1947

And forty-four lithographs, including "Le Ventre Législatif" (Delteil no. 131)

DAVID, HERMINE (French Contemporary)

STREET IN FRANCE
oil on mounted paper 26½ × 20½, *unsigned*

DAVIES, ARTHUR B. (American 1862–1928)*

ALONG THE ERIE CANAL   *Plate 86*
canvas 18 × 40, *signed* l.l.: A. B. Davies 1890
References: "Arthur B. Davies" (Phillips Gallery, 1925) illus.; The Arts,
February 1929, illus.; Oliver W. Larkin "Art and Life in America",
p. 335; Jerome Mellquist "The Emergence of an American Art" (1942),
illus. p. 121; World Book Encyclopedia (1944), illus. in color; John
Walker and Macgill James "Great American Paintings from Smibert
to Bellows", illus. in color
Exhibited: Metropolitan Museum of Art, Davies Memorial Exh., 1930;
Museum of Modern Art, 1933; Renaissance Society, Chicago, 1933;
Cleveland Museum of Art, "American Painting from 1860 until Today",
1937; Whitney Museum of American Art, 1938; Metropolitan Museum
of Art "Life in America", 1939, illus. p. 66; Museum of Modern Art
"Romantic Painting in America", 1943, illus. p. 85; Tate Gallery,
London, Exh. of American Painting, 1946; Carnegie Institute, Pittsburgh
"Survey of American Painting", 1940; Munson-Williams-Proctor Insti-
tute, Utica, 1948, illus. in bulletin

CHILDREN, DOGS AND PONY
canvas 22 × 17, *signed* l.l.: A. B. Davies
Exhibited: Metropolitan Museum of Art, Davies Memorial Exh., 1930

CITY GIRLS AND COUNTRY BOY
canvas 24 × 18, *unsigned*
Exhibited: Baltimore Museum of Art, 1924

DEW DROPS
canvas 13 × 15, *signed* l.l.: A. B. Davies

THE FLOOD   *Plate 87b*
canvas 18 × 30, *signed* l.r.: A. B. Davies
Exhibited: Macbeth Gallery, 1908, original exh. of "The Eight"; Brooklyn
Museum, Exh. of "The Eight", 1943

THE HESITATION OF ORESTES
canvas 26×40, *signed* l.l.: A. B. Davies
Exhibited: Baltimore Museum of Art, 1927; Metropolitan Museum of Art, Davies Memorial Exh., 1930, no. 73, illus. in cat.; Baltimore Museum of Art "The Greek Tradition", 1939

HORSES OF ATTICA
canvas 8¼×15¼, *signed* l.l.: A. B. Davies
Exhibited: Metropolitan Museum of Art, Davies Memorial Exh., 1930, no. 61, illus. in cat.

MANY WATERS
canvas 17×22, *signed* l.l.: A. B. Davies
Exhibited: Macbeth Gallery, 1908, original exh. of "The Eight"; Carnegie Institute "A Century of American Landscape Painting", 1939; Brooklyn Museum, Exh. of "The Eight", 1943

SPRINGTIME OF DELIGHT   *Plate 87a*
canvas 18×40, *signed* l.l.: A. B. Davies 1906
Exhibited: Exhibition of American Painting, Venice, 1924; Arts Club of Chicago, Ryder-Davies Exh., 1946

TISSUE PARNASSIAN
oil and charcoal on canvas 26×40, *signed* l.l.: A. B. Davies
References: The Arts, February 1929, p. 90, illus.
Exhibited: Metropolitan Museum of Art, Davies Memorial Exh., 1930, no. 184, illus. in cat.

VIOLA OBLIGATO
(Gift of Mrs. Wendell T. Bush)
wood panel 14×11½, *signed* l.r.: A. B. Davies
Exhibited: Metropolitan Museum of Art, Davies Memorial Exh., 1930

VISIONS OF GLORY
canvas 11×16, *painted c.* 1896, *signed* l.r.c.: A. B. Davies

THE VOYAGE
canvas 13¼×16¼, *signed* l.l.c.: A. B. Davies

DAVIS, STUART (American Contemporary)

BLUE CAFÉ
canvas $18\frac{1}{2} \times 21\frac{3}{4}$, *painted* 1928, *signed* u.r.: Stuart Davis
Exhibited: Museum of Modern Art, Stuart Davis Exh., 1945

BOATS
canvas 18×22, *signed* u.l.: Stuart Davis, July 1930

CORNER CAFÉ   *Plate 214b*
canvas 15×19, *signed* u.r.: Stuart Davis

EGG BEATER No. 1
canvas $27 \times 38\frac{1}{4}$, *painted* 1927, *signed* u.r.: Stuart Davis
Exhibited: Cincinnati Society of Modern Art, Davis-Hartley Exh., 1941;
Museum of Modern Art, Stuart Davis Exh., 1945; Baltimore Museum of
Art, Stuart Davis Exh., 1946

MANDOLIN AND SAW
canvas 26×34, *painted* 1930, *signed* u.r.: Stuart Davis

And two lithographs

DECAMPS, ALEXANDRE GABRIEL (French 1803–1860)

INTERIOR OF A TURKISH CAFÉ
canvas $12\frac{1}{2} \times 16$, *signed* l.l.: D C
Collections: Ichabod Williams, New York
Exhibited: Rochester Memorial Art Gallery, 1936

DEGAS, EDGAR (French 1834-1917)*

BALLET REHEARSAL (La Salle de Danse)   *Plate 58*
canvas $15 \times 34\frac{1}{2}$, *painted* c. 1891, *signed* l.l.: Degas
Collections: Clarke, New York
References: Meier-Graefe "Degas", illus. pl. 52; L'Amour de L'Art,
July 1931, p. 280 illus.; P. A. Lemoisne "Degas et son Oeuvre" (1946),
vol. III, no. 1107, illus.
Exhibited: Yale University Art Gallery, 1937; Wildenstein, New York,
Degas Exh., 1949

DANCERS AT THE BAR (Danseuses à la Barre) Color Repr. and Plate 59
canvas 51 × 38, *painted c.* 1888, *signed* l.r.: Degas
Collections: Durand-Ruel, Paris; A. Vollard, Paris; Jacques Seligmann, Paris (private collection); Mrs. W. A. Harriman, New York
References: Atelier Degas, 1st sale, no. 93, illus. in cat.; Jacques Seligmann Sales Cat., 1921, no. 65, illus.; P. A. Lemoisne "Degas et son Oeuvre", vol. III, no. 807, illus.
Exhibited: Paul Rosenberg, New York "The 19th Century Heritage", March 1950; Yale University Art Gallery, April–May 1950

REFLECTION (La Mélancolie)   *Plate 57*
canvas 7½ × 9⅝, *painted c.* 1874, *signed* l.r.: Degas
Collections: Georges Viau, Paris; Wilhelm Hansen, Copenhagen; D. W. T. Cargill, Scotland
References: A. Alexandre, Les Arts, August 1912, illus.; Femina, December 1917, illus.; Paul Jamot "Degas" p. 137, illus. pl. 21*b*; Ragnar Hoppe "Degas", illus.; P. A. Lemoisne "Degas et son Oeuvre", vol. III, no. 357, illus.
Exhibited: Centennial Exhibition of French Art, Paris, 1900; French Art, Geneva, 1918, no. 2 of cat.; "Works by Degas", Glasgow and London, 1928, no. 10 of cat.; Musée de l'Orangerie, Paris, "Degas", 1931, no. 57 of cat.; Royal Academy, London, Exh. of French Art, 1932, no. 562 of cat.; Musée de l'Orangerie, Paris, "Degas", 1937, no. 19 of cat.

AFTER THE BATH (La Sortie du Bain)   *Plate 60*
pastel 30 × 32½, *painted c.* 1895–98, *unsigned*
Collections: A. Vollard, Paris; Yolande Mazuc, Venezuela
References: First Degas Sale catalogue, 1918, p. 136, no. 255, illus.; P. A. Lemoisne "Degas et son Oeuvre", no. 1204, illus.
Exhibited: Wildenstein, New York, loan exh. of Degas, 1949, p. 65, no. 84

WOMEN COMBING THEIR HAIR (Femmes se Peignant)   *Plate 56*
oil on paper, mounted on canvas 12¼ × 17¾, *painted c.* 1875–76, *signed* l.r.: Degas
Collections: Henri Lerolle, Paris
References: Meier-Graefe "Degas", pl. 39; Henri Hertz "Degas", Art et Esthetique, 1920, pl. 8; C. Mauclair "Degas", p. 88, illus.; P. A. Lemoisne "Degas et son Oeuvre", no. 376, illus.
Exhibited: Galerie Georges Petit, Paris, 1924, "Degas", no. 56, illus.;

Galerie Paul Rosenberg, Paris, 1931, "Great Masters of the 19th Century"; Palais des Beaux-Arts, Brussels, 1935, "L'Impressionisme", no. 15, illus.; New-Burlington Galleries, London, 1936, "Masters of French 19th Century Painting", no. 62; Musée de l'Orangerie, Paris, 1937, "Degas", no. 23, illus.; Cleveland Museum of Art, Degas Exh., 1947; Wildenstein, New York, Degas Exh., 1949; Yale University Art Gallery, 1950, "19th Century French Paintings", no. 6, illus. in cat.

DELACROIX, EUGÈNE (French 1798–1863)

HERCULES AND ALCESTIS (Hercule Ramenant Alceste des Enfers)   Plate 19
canvas mounted on panel $12\frac{1}{8} \times 19\frac{1}{2}$, *signed* l.l.c.: Eug. Delacroix 1862
Collections: Ernest Cronier; Chéramy; Dikran Kélékian
References: Arsène Alexandre "The Kélékian Collection", Kélékian Collection Catalogue (1920), p. 7; Kélékian Collection Catalogue, illus. pl. 39; R. Escholier "Delacroix, Peintre, Graveur, Écrivain" (1929), illus. opp. p. 86
Exhibited: Virginia Museum of Fine Arts, October–November 1950

HORSES COMING OUT OF THE SEA   Plate 18
canvas $19\frac{3}{4} \times 24$, *signed* l.r.: Eug. Delacroix 1860
Collections: Marquis de Lau; Edwards; Fenien; Faure; Laurent-Richard; Alfred Mame, Tours; Esnault-Pelterie; Baron Denys-Cochin; Emile Staub-Terlinden, Switzerland
References: Alfred Robaut "L'Oeuvre Complet de Delacroix" (1885), no. 1410, p. 378; Les Arts, June 1906, p. 6, illus. p. 8; Etienne Moreau-Nelaton "Delacroix raconté par lui-même" (1916), p. 195, illus. 409; Raymond Escholier "Delacroix", no. 111, p. 151; Raymond Escholier "Delacroix, Peintre, Graveur, Écrivain" (1929), p. 255, illus. p. 253; Pierre Courthion "L'Art français dans les collections privées en Suisse", L'Amour de l'Art, February 1926, p. 39, illus.; L'Arte, January 1931, illus. p. 81; Louis Hourticq "Delacroix" (1930), illus. p. 177; Formes, May 1932, illus. opp. p. 270; "La Peinture française du XIXe siècle en Suisse" (1938), no. 53, pp. 26–27
Exhibited: École des Beaux-Arts, Paris, Exposition Delacroix, 1885, no. 136; Musée du Louvre, Exposition Delacroix, 1930, no. 189; Museum of Art and History, Geneva, 1937; Wildenstein, New York, Delacroix Exh., 1944, no. 42, illus. in cat.; Paul Rosenberg, New York, Delacroix-Renoir Exh., 1948, no. 13

cardboard panel $17\frac{1}{4} \times 11\frac{1}{2}$, *painted c.* 1832, *unsigned*
Collections: Hermann, 1879; Perreau; Champfleury; Chéramy; Kélékian
References: Robaut "L'Oeuvre" (1885), no. 386; Meier-Graefe "Delacroix"
(1922), no. 118; Escholier "Delacroix" (1927), p. 168, illus. p. 167; Roger
Fry "Modern Paintings in a Collection of Ancient Art", Burlington
Magazine, December 1920, reprinted in Kélékian Sales Cat., 1922; Hans
Tietze "Masterpieces of European Painting in American Collections",
illus. p. 270; Sheldon Cheney "A World History of Art", p. 810; "The
Story of Modern Art", illus. p. 31; Jacques Barzun "Romanticism:
Definition of a Period", Magazine of Art, November 1949, illus. p. 244
Exhibited: Musée de Louvre, Exposition Delacroix, 1930, no. 60a; Art
Institute of Chicago, Delacroix Exh., 1930, no. 13; M. Knoedler "Gros,
Géricault, Delacroix", 1938, no. 43; Wildenstein, New York "The
French Revolution", 1943, no. 423; Virginia Museum of Fine Arts, 1947

LE ROY RENÉ
pencil and wash drawing 13×18, *dated* l.l.c.; 1830; *inscribed* l.r.c.:
"Le Roy René"

DE MARTINI, JOSEPH (American Contemporary)

QUARRY BATHERS No. 3
canvas 24×30, *painted c.* 1935, *signed* l.r.: Joseph de Martini

SELF PORTRAIT
canvas 48×30, *painted c.* 1943, *signed* l.r.: Joseph de Martini

DEMUTH, CHARLES (American 1883–1935)

EGG PLANT *Plate 198b*
watercolor 12×18, *unsigned*

MONUMENT, BERMUDA
watercolor 14×10, *signed* l.l.: C. Demuth 1917
Exhibited: Whitney Museum of American Art, Demuth Memorial Exh.,
December 1937–January 1938; Museum of Modern Art, Demuth Exh.,
1950

RED CHIMNEYS   *Plate 198a*
watercolor 9¾ × 13¾, *signed* l.l.c.: C. Demuth 1918
Exhibited: Whitney Museum of American Art, Demuth Memorial Exh.,
December 1937–January 1938; Museum of Modern Art, Demuth Exh.,
1950

DERAIN, ANDRÉ (French Contemporary)

DECORATIVE LANDSCAPE   *Plate 160*
canvas 45 × 34, *signed* l.r.: Derain 1900
References: Creative Art, May 1929, illus. p. 49

A BRUNETTE   *Plate 182a*
canvas 14 × 11, *signed* l.r.: Derain

HEAD OF A YOUNG WOMAN
canvas 18¼ × 15, *signed* l.r.: A. Derain

MANO, THE DANCER
canvas 35½ × 28½, *painted* 1928, *signed* l.r.: Derain
Exhibited: Museum of Modern Art "Painting in Paris", 1930, no. 29;
Arts Club of Chicago, Derain Exh., 1946, no. 17

SOUTHERN FRANCE   *Plate 183*
canvas 30 × 36, *painted* 1927, *signed* l.r.: A. Derain
Exhibited: Museum of Modern Art "Painting in Paris", 1930, no. 25,
illus. in cat.; Renaissance Society, Chicago, 1933; Metropolitan Museum
of Art, 1934; Golden Gate International Exposition, San Francisco,
1939, no. 13, illus. in cat.; Worcester Art Museum "The Art of the Third
Republic, 1870–1940", 1941, no. 31, illus. in cat.; Art News, February
15, 1941, illus. p. 28; Arts Club of Chicago, Derain Exh., 1946;
University of Virginia, 1948

DESPIAU, CHARLES (French 1874–1946)

HEAD OF MME. DERAIN   *Plate 153*
plaster 13 in. high on base 6 × 6, *signed* on rear of base: C. Despiau, 1922
References: Charles Seymour, Jr. "Tradition and Experiment in Modern
Sculpture" (1949), p. 38, frontis.

SEATED NUDE
sanguine drawing $14\frac{1}{4} \times 10\frac{1}{4}$, *signed* u.r.: C. Despiau

DICKINSON, PRESTON (American 1891–1930)

ALONG THE RIVER   *Plate 214a*
pastel and ink $15 \times 22\frac{1}{2}$, *signed* l.l.: Preston Dickinson

DECANTER AND BOTTLES
pastel $23\frac{1}{2} \times 13$, *signed* l.r.: Preston Dickinson

MY HOUSE
tempera $10\frac{1}{4} \times 8$, *signed* l.l.c.: Dickinson

OLD QUARTER, QUEBEC
canvas 24×30, *signed* l.r.: Preston Dickinson 27
Exhibited: American Exh., Stockholm, Copenhagen, Munich, 1930

STREET IN QUEBEC
canvas 19×30, *signed* l.r.: Preston Dickinson

WINTER, HARLEM RIVER
canvas 20×30, *signed* l.l.: Preston Dickinson
Exhibited: Tate Gallery, London, Exh. of American Paintings, 1946

DIEDERICH, HUNT (American Contemporary)

SPANISH RIDER
bronze 17 in. high, *signed* on base: H D

DOUGHERTY, PAUL (American 1877–1947)

BRIDGE IN SPAIN
watercolor 14×20, *unsigned*

PORTO RICO
watercolor $13\frac{1}{2} \times 19\frac{1}{2}$, *signed* l.r.: Paul Dougherty

STORM VOICES
canvas 36×48, *signed* l.l.: Paul Dougherty 1912

DOVE, ARTHUR G. (American 1880–1946)*

COAL CARRIER
canvas 20×26, *painted c.* 1930, *signed* l.r.: Dove
Exhibited: Philadelphia Museum of Art, 1931

COWS IN PASTURE
Plate 188
canvas 20×28, *painted* 1935, *signed* l.c.: Dove
References: Duncan Phillips "Arthur G. Dove, 1880–1946", Magazine of Art, May 1947, p. 195

ELECTRIC PEACH ORCHARD
Plate 186a
canvas 20×28, *painted* 1935, *signed* l.c.: Dove
Exhibited: Cleveland Museum of Art, 1935; South America, Traveling Exh. of Contemporary North American Painting, 1941

FLOUR MILL ABSTRACTION
Plate 190
canvas 26×16, *painted* 1938, *signed* l.c.: Dove
References: Duncan Phillips "Arthur G. Dove, 1880–1946", Magazine of Art, May 1947, p. 196, illus. p. 192
Exhibited: Baltimore Museum of Art, 1940; Tate Gallery, London, Exh. of American Paintings, 1946; Downtown Gallery, Dove Retrospective Exh., 1947

GOLDEN STORM
Plate 185
wood panel 18½×20½, *painted c.* 1926, *unsigned*
References: Duncan Phillips "Arthur G. Dove, 1880–1946", Magazine of Art, May 1947, p. 195; C. Law Watkins "The Language of Design", illus. p. 75
Exhibited: Downtown Gallery, Dove Retrospective Exh., 1947; Stedelijk Museum, Amsterdam, 1950

GREEN AND GOLD AND BROWN
canvas 18×27, *painted* 1941, *signed* l.c.: Dove
References: Duncan Phillips "Arthur G. Dove, 1880–1946", Magazine of Art, May 1947, p. 197, illus.
Exhibited: City Art Museum, St. Louis, "Trends in American Painting of Today", 1942, no. 72; California Palace of the Legion of Honor, San Francisco "Contemporary American Painting", 1945

HUNTINGTON HARBOR
Plate 184a
collage 12×9½, *executed* 1926, *unsigned*
Exhibited: Detroit Institute of Arts, 1944

INDIAN ONE
canvas 18×24, *painted* 1943, *signed* l.c.: Dove

LIFE GOES ON   *Plate 186b*
canvas 18×24, *painted* 1934, *signed* l.c.: Dove
Exhibited: George Walter Vincent Smith Art Museum, Springfield, 1935;
Detroit Institute of Arts, 1944

MORNING SUN
canvas 20×28, *painted* 1935, *signed* l.c.: Dove
Exhibited: Syracuse Museum, 1939; Golden Gate International Exposition, San Francisco, 1940, no. 1325; Downtown Gallery, Dove Retrospective Exh., 1947

GOIN' FISHIN'
collage 19½×24, *executed* 1925, *unsigned*
References: Jerome Mellquist "The Emergence of an American Art",
p. 365; Duncan Phillips "Arthur G. Dove, 1880–1946", Magazine of
Art, May 1947, pp. 194–95
Exhibited: Musée du Jeu de Paume, Paris, Exh. of American Painting,
1938, no. 46, pl. 32 in illus. cat.; Museum of Modern Art, "Art in Our
Time", 1939, no. 198, illus.; Downtown Gallery, Dove Restrospective
Exh., 1947; California Palace of the Legion of Honor, "Illusionism and
Trompe L'Oeil", 1949, illus. p. 44 in cat.; "Abstract Painting and
Sculpture in America", Museum of Modern Art, 1951, no. 22, illus.
p. 63 in cat.

POZZUOLI RED
canvas 22×36, *painted* 1941, *signed* l.c.: Dove

PRIMITIVE MUSIC
canvas 18×24, *painted* 1944, *signed* l.c.: Dove
Exhibited: Downtown Gallery, Dove Retrospective Exh., 1947

RAIN OR SNOW   *Plate 191*
canvas 35×25, *painted* 1943, *signed* l.c.: Dove
Exhibited: Art Gallery of Toronto, 1945

RED BARGE, REFLECTIONS
canvas 30×40, *painted* 1932, *signed* l.c.: Dove
References: Forbes Watson "American Painting Today" (1939), illus.

p. 41; "America and Alfred Stieglitz", pl. x; Rosamund Frost "Contemporary Art" (1942), p. 183; Jerome Mellquist "The Emergence of an American Art" (1942), illus. facing p. 365; Duncan Phillips "Arthur G. Dove, 1880–1946", Magazine of Art, May 1947, illus. p. 196
Exhibited: Art Institute of Chicago, 1934; Albright Art Gallery, Buffalo, 1936; Syracuse Museum of Fine Arts, 1939; Dallas Museum of Fine Arts "Survey of American Painting", 1946; Corcoran Gallery of Art "De Gustibus", January–February 1949

RED SUN
canvas 24×33½, *painted* 1935, *signed* l.c.: Dove
References: C. Law Watkins "The Language of Design", illus. p. 121
Exhibited: City Art Museum, St. Louis, 1942

REMINISCENCE
canvas 15×21, *painted* 1937, *signed* l.c.: Dove
References: Duncan Phillips "Arthur G. Dove, 1880–1946", Magazine of Art, May 1947, pp. 195–6

RISE OF THE FULL MOON   *Plate 189*
canvas 18×26, *painted* 1937, *signed* l.c.: Dove

ROSE AND LOCUST STUMP
canvas 24×32, *painted* 1944, *signed* l.c.: Dove

SAND BARGE
wood panel 30×40, *painted* 1930, *signed* l.r.: Dove
Exhibited: Traveling exhibition "American Painting in Our Century", 1949; "Abstract Painting and Sculpture in America", Museum of Modern Art, 1951, no. 23, illus. p. 93 in cat.

SHORE FRONT
canvas 22×36, *painted* 1938, *signed* l.c.: Dove
Exhibited: Syracuse Museum of Fine Arts, 1939; Pennsylvania Academy of Fine Arts, 1945

WATERFALL
composition panel 10×8, *painted* 1925, *unsigned*
References: Sheldon Cheney "The Story of Modern Art" (1945), illus. p. 618

WOODPECKER   *Plate 193b*
canvas 15×21, *painted* 1941, *signed* l.c.: Dove

And a group of alternate paintings and a group of watercolors

DU BOIS, GUY PÈNE (American Contemporary)

BLUE ARMCHAIR
wood panel 25×20, *signed* l.r.: Guy Pène du Bois 23

SOLDIER AND PEASANT
wood panel 22×18½, *signed* l.l.: Guy Pène du Bois 27

DUFY, RAOUL (French Contemporary)

THE ARTIST'S STUDIO   Plate 155
canvas 46¾×58¾, *signed* l.l.: Raoul Dufy 1935

CHÂTEAU AND HORSES   Plate 154b
canvas 23¾×28¾, *signed* l.l.: Raoul Dufy 1930

EPSOM
watercolor 19×25, *signed* l.r.: Raoul Dufy, Epsom 1935
Exhibited: Arts Club of Chicago, "Raoul Dufy", 1941

HOTEL SUBES
canvas 21×25½, *signed* l.r.: Raoul Dufy
Exhibited: Arts Club of Chicago, "Raoul Dufy", 1941

JOINVILLE   Plate 154a
canvas 14⅞×36¼, *signed* l.r.c.: Raoul Dufy, 1938

THE OPERA, PARIS   Plate 157
watercolor and gouache 21½×27¼, *signed* l.r.: Raoul Dufy
References: Fortune Magazine, October 1945, illus. in color, p. 173
Exhibited: Institute of Contemporary Art, Boston, 1945

POLO
watercolor 19×24¾, *signed* l.r.c.: Raoul Dufy

SEASIDE MOTIFS
watercolor and gouache 19×25, *signed* l.l.c.: Raoul Dufy

VERSAILLES   Plate 156
watercolor 19×25½, *painted* 1936, *signed* l.r.c.: Raoul Dufy
References: Fortune Magazine, October 1945, illus. in color p. 172

35

EAKINS, THOMAS (American 1844–1916)

MISS VAN BUREN   Plate 53
canvas 45 × 32, *painted c. 1889–91, unsigned*
Collections: Miss Amelia C. Van Buren
References: Creative Art, May 1929, illus. p. 22; Parnassus, May 1930,
cover illus.; Magazine of Art, November 1933, illus. p. 503; Lloyd
Goodrich "Thomas Eakins" (1933), illus.; Roland McKinney "Thomas
Eakins" (1942), illus.; JohnWalker and Macgill James "Great American
Paintings from Smibert to Bellows" (1943), illus.
Exhibited: Museum of Modern Art, Homer-Ryder-Eakins Exh., May
1930, no. 102, illus.; Metropolitan Museum of Art, 1932; Museum of
Modern Art, "Art in Our Time", 1939, no. 33, illus. in cat.; Carnegie
Institute, Eakins Centennial Exh., 1945, no. 90, illus. in cat.; Tate
Gallery, London, Exh. of American Paintings, 1946

EILSHEMIUS, LOUIS (American 1864–1941)*

APPROACHING STORM
composition panel 23 × 27, *signed* l.l.: Elshemus 1890
References: William Schack "And He Sat Among the Ashes" (1939),
p. 146
Exhibited: Carnegie Institute, "Survey of American Painting", 1940

BALCONY VIEW   Plate 90
composition panel 18½ × 13½, *painted* 1900, *signed* l.r.: Elshemus

BRIDGE FOR FISHING   Plate 91
canvas 18 × 35, *signed* l.r.: Elshemus

CABS FOR HIRE   Plate 93
composition panel 22 × 28, *signed* l.l.: Eilshemus
References: William Schack "And He Sat Among the Ashes", p. 147,
illus. p. 198
Exhibited: Tate Gallery, London, Exh. of American Paintings, 1946

CHILDREN ON THE BEACH
masonite panel 20 × 30, *signed* l.r.: Elshemus 1909

THE DREAM
composition panel 30¾ × 41½, *signed* l.r.: 1917 Eilshemius

EVENING LIGHT BY THE SEA
paper⁄board panel $8\frac{5}{8} \times 23\frac{3}{4}$, *signed* l.r.: Eilshemius, *dated* l.l.: 1918

KINGSBRIDGE
paper⁄board panel 20×30, *signed* l.l.: Eilshemius 1909
References: William Schack "And He Sat Among the Ashes", p. 224

MADGE IN THE MORNING   *Plate 92*
paper⁄board panel $13\frac{1}{4} \times 8$, *signed* l.r.: Elshemus
References: Parnassus, October 1935, "Eilshemius" by William Schack, pp. 6–8, illus.
Exhibited: Yale University Art Gallery, 1936

THE REJECTED SUITOR   *Plate 94*
masonite panel $20\frac{1}{2} \times 30\frac{1}{2}$, *signed* l.r.: Eilshemius; *dated* l.l.: 1915
References: Jean Charlot "Louis Eilshemius", Hound and Horn, January–March 1933, p. 244; William Schack "And He Sat Among the Ashes", illus. p. 218

SAMOA
paper⁄board panel $23 \times 26\frac{3}{4}$, *signed* l.r.: Eilshemus 1907
Exhibited: Baltimore Museum of Art, 1927; Syracuse Museum of Fine Arts, 1939

STREET IN LUGANO
canvas 24×18, *painted* 1893, *signed* l.l.: Elshemus

SURF AND BOAT
paper⁄board panel $9\frac{1}{4} \times 17\frac{1}{4}$, *signed* l.r.: Eilshemius

TWILIGHT IN SAMOA
canvas 20×30, *signed* l.r.: Elshemus

VERANDAH IN SPRING
paper⁄board panel $13\frac{1}{4} \times 7\frac{3}{8}$, *signed* l.r.: Elshemus

YUMA, ARIZONA   *Plate 89*
canvas 12×16, *painted* 1890, *signed* l.l.: Elshemus
References: Duncan Phillips "The Duality of Eilshemius", Magazine of Art, December 1939; pp. 694–97, 724–27 contain references to many of the paintings listed above

FAGGI, ALFEO (Italian Contemporary)

HEAD OF NOGUCHI
bronze 18½ in. high, *signed* on base at side: A. Faggi

FANTIN-LATOUR, HENRI (French 1836–1904)

DAWN
canvas 14¼×15, *signed* l.l.: Fantin

MANET IN HIS STUDIO   Plate 38b
canvas 11½×13½, *painted* 1870, *signed* l.l.: Fantin

PEACHES
canvas 7½×11, *signed* u.l.: Fantin 69

And a group of lithographs

FAUTRIER, JEAN (French Contemporary)

FLOWERS OF DISASTER
canvas 21¼25×¾, *signed* l.l.: Fautrier

FEININGER, LYONEL (American Contemporary)

VILLAGE
canvas 16¾×28½, *painted* 1927, *signed* l.r.: Feininger

WATERFRONT
watercolor 11½×18, *signed* l.l.: Feininger, *dated* l.r.: 5.vii.42
Exhibited: Museum of Modern Art, Feininger-Hartley Exh., 1944

FIENE, ERNEST (American Contemporary)

FALL OF OLD HOUSES
canvas 26×36, *signed* l.r.: Ernest Fiene

FLANNERY, VAUGHN (American Contemporary)

THE GOVERNOR'S CUP   *Plate 232a*
wood panel $27\frac{7}{8} \times 39\frac{7}{8}$, *signed* l.r.: V F

TEN BROECK
canvas 17×24, *unsigned*
Exhibited: Carnegie Institute, Pittsburgh, 29th International Exh., 1930

FRAGONARD, JEAN HONORÉ (French 1732–1806)

Two drawings for Ariosto's "Orlando Furioso":

ODORICO KILLS COREBO
pencil and sepia wash $15\frac{1}{4} \times 9\frac{1}{2}$, *unsigned*

RODOMONTE LEAPS ACROSS THE MOAT   *Plate 8*
pencil and sepia wash $16 \times 11\frac{1}{8}$
References: National Gallery, Washington, and Harvard College Library
edition of "Fragonard Drawings for Ariosto", 1945, nos. 93 & 110

FRESNAYE, ROGER DE LA (French 1885–1925)

EMBLEMS (La Mappemonde)   *Plate 161*
canvas $35 \times 78\frac{3}{4}$, *painted c.* 1912, *unsigned*
Collections: de Miré, Paris
References: Paul Chadourne "Notes sur Roger de la Fresnaye", Cahiers
d'Art (no. 8, 1928), p. 314, illus. p. 313; A. Basler & C. Kunstler "The
Moderns" (1931), pl. 31; Raymond Cogniat "Le Neo-Cubisme, Roger
de la Fresnaye", L'Amour de l'Art, December 1933, illus. p. 249;
Germain Seligman "Roger de la Fresnaye"; E. Nebelthau "Roger de la
Fresnaye", illus.; René Huyghe "L'Histoire de l'Art Contemporain"
(1935), fig. 314; Duncan Phillips, foreword to de la Fresnaye Exhibition
catalogue, The Phillips Gallery, January 1944; Ethlyne J. & Germain
Seligman "Roger de la Fresnaye and Juan Gris", The Art Quarterly,
Spring 1949, p. 148
Exhibited: Petit Palais, Paris "Les Maîtres de l'Art Indépendant", 1937,
no. 9; Arts Club of Chicago, de la Fresnaye Exh., December 1943, no. 24;
Toledo Museum of Art, October–December 1946; Art Gallery of
Toronto, January–February 1947, "The Spirit of Modern France"

FRIEDMAN, ARNOLD (American 1879–1947)

THE BROWN DERBY
canvas 30×24, *signed* l.r.: Friedman

FULLER, GEORGE (American 1822–1884)

IDEAL HEAD   *Plate 42*
canvas 24×20, *signed* l.r.: G. Fuller
Collections: F. M. Weld

GABO, NAUM (Russian-American Contemporary)

LINEAR CONSTRUCTION, VARIATION   *Plate 243*
plastic and nylon thread construction, *executed* 1942–43, *unsigned*
References: Charles Seymour, Jr. "Tradition and Experiment in Modern
Sculpture", illus. p. 58
Exhibited: Museum of Modern Art, Gabo-Pevsner Exh., 1948, illus. in
cat., pp. 44–45

GALLATIN, A. E. (American Contemporary)

ABSTRACTION
oil and paper collage on canvas board $18\frac{3}{4} \times 14\frac{1}{2}$, *signed* on back: A. E.
Gallatin Oct. 1941

GATCH, LEE (American Contemporary)*

CAN-CAN
canvas 18×28, *painted* 1943, *signed* l.r.: Gatch

CITY AT EVENING
canvas 18×25, *painted* 1933, *signed* l.l.: Gatch
Exhibited: Carnegie Institute, Pittsburgh, 1941

FIRE ON THE DOCKS
canvas 8×30, *painted* 1935, *signed* l.r.: Gatch

INDUSTRIAL NIGHT   *Plate 236b*
canvas 18×40, *painted* 1948, *signed* l.r.: Gatch
References: Art News, March 1949, p. 39, illus. in color

MARCHING HIGHLANDERS   *Plate 236a*
canvas 17×30, *painted* 1933, *signed* l.r.: Gatch

ORIENTALS AT THE RACES
canvas 14×48½, *painted* 1939, *signed* l.r.: Lee Gatch
Exhibited: Biennale, Venice, 1950

THREE CANDIDATES FOR ELECTION   *Plate 237*
canvas 36×21, *painted* 1948, *signed* l.r.: Gatch
Exhibited: Biennale, Venice, 1950

WINTER HOUSE
wood panel 7½×12⅝, *signed* l.r.: Gatch

References: Duncan Phillips "Lee Gatch", Magazine of Art, December
1949, pp. 282–87, refers to many of the Gatch paintings listed above
(illus.)

GÉRICAULT, THÉODORE (French 1791–1824)

TWO HORSES   *Plate 17*
canvas 10¼×16, *unsigned*
Collections: Eugène Delacroix; M. Foinard; Duc de Trévise, Paris;
R. Goetz, New York
Exhibited: Exposition Centenaire de Géricault chez Charpentier, Paris,
1923; Exposition Géricault, Bernheim Jeune, Paris, 1923

GIORGIONE (?) (Italian 1477?–1510)

THE HOUR GLASS   *Frontispiece in Color*
wood panel 4¾×7½, *unsigned*   *and Plate 1*
Collections: Pulszky, Budapest
Exhibited: Johns Hopkins University, Baltimore, "Giorgione and His
Circle", 1942, no. 1, illus. pl. 1 in cat.; Brooklyn Museum, 1945

GLACKENS, WILLIAM (American 1870–1938)

BATHERS AT BELLPORT
canvas 25 × 30, *painted c.* 1920, *signed* l.l.: W. Glackens

GOGH, VINCENT VAN (Dutch 1853–1890)

ENTRANCE TO THE PUBLIC GARDENS AT ARLES   *Plate 64*
canvas $28\frac{1}{2} \times 35\frac{5}{8}$, *painted* 1888, *unsigned*
Collections: Mme. Thea Sternheim, Uttwil; Prince de Wagram, Paris; Arthur Sachs, New York
References: Vincent Van Gogh "Letters to his Brother", vol. III, letter 538, p. 177, letter 539, p. 179; J. B. De La Faille "Vincent Van Gogh" (1928) no. 566; (1938) no. 553; Duncan Phillips "The Artist Sees Differently", vol. I, pp. 123–24, illus. in color opp. p. 122; Duncan Phillips, article on Van Gogh and this painting written to accompany color reproduction, Twin Print, No. 24, 1943; C. Law Watkins "The Language of Design", p. 149, illus. p. 146; M. A. Leblond "Peintres de race", illus. p. 17; Kurt Pfister "Vincent van Gogh", pl. 29; G. Hartlaub "Vincent van Gogh", illus.; Aesculape, June 1926, illus. p. 156; Der Cicerone, August 1922, illus. p. 648; V. Doiteau & E. Leroy "La Folie de van Gogh", illus. p. 45; F. Fels "Van Gogh", illus. p. 205; Das Kunstblatt, October 1918, illus. p. 314; Art News, October 15, 1943, illus. in color, p. 16
Exhibited: Galerie Bernheim Jeune, Paris, Exposition Van Gogh, 1901; Cologne, International Exhibition, 1912, no. 92, illus. in cat.; Paul Cassirer, Berlin, 1914, no. 83; Musée de Winterthur, 1922, no. 53; Kunsthalle, Basle, 1924, no. 57; Kunsthaus, Zürich, 1924, no. 37; Art Institute of Chicago, Century of Progress Exh., 1933, no. 383; Museum of Modern Art, Opening Exhibition, November 1929, no. 82, illus. in cat.; Baltimore Museum of Art, 1934; Museum of Modern Art, Van Gogh Exh., January 1937; New York World's Fair "Masterpieces of Art", 1940, no. 362, illus. p. 246; Wildenstein, New York, Van Gogh Exh., 1943, no. 38, illus. p. 79; Cleveland Museum of Art, Van Gogh Exh., 1948, no. 13, illus. pl. XI; Metropolitan Museum of Art, Art Institute of Chicago, Van Gogh Exh., 1949–50, cat. no. 79, illus. p. 59; Philadelphia Museum of Art, Diamond Jubilee Exh., November 1950–February 1951, no. 91 illus. in cat.

canvas 28 × 36⅝, *painted* 1889, *unsigned*

Collections: H. von Tschudi, Munich; Mme. J. van Gogh-Bonger, Amsterdam; Miss Dorothy Sturges, Providence; Miss Elizabeth Hudson, Syracuse

References: J.-B. De la Faille "Van Gogh" (1938) no. 667; (1928) no. 657; Vincent van Gogh "Letters to his Brother", vol. III, letter 621, p. 406; Th. van Gogh "Lettres à son Frère Vincent", letter 24, p. 84; J. Meier-Graefe "Vincent van Gogh", illus. p. 33; "Vincent", vol. II, pl. 93; Kurt Pfister "Vincent van Gogh", pl. 22; Albert Dreyfus, Die Kunst, December 1913, illus. p. 103; Louis Piérard "La Vie Tragique de Vincent van Gogh", illus. p. 80; M. Deri "Die Malerei im XIX Jahrh.", vol. II, pl. 56; Scherjon & de Gruyter "Van Gogh's Great Period" (1937), p. 273; Vincent van Gogh "Further Letters of Vincent van Gogh to His Brother", letter 618

Exhibited: Munich, Neue Staatsgalerie; Municipal Museum, Amsterdam, 1905, no. 190; Rhode Island School of Design, 1932; Art Institute of Chicago, Century of Progress Exhibition, 1933, no. 381, illus. in cat.; Wildenstein, New York, Van Gogh Exh., 1943, no. 54, illus. p. 95 in cat.; Cleveland Museum of Art, "Vincent van Gogh", 1948, no. 26, illus. pl. XXII in cat.

DR. GACHET
etching 7 × 5¾, *unsigned, dated* on plate u.r.: 15 mai 90

GOLDTHWAITE, ANNE (American 1875–1944)

CATALPA IN BLOOM
canvas 24 × 29, *signed* l.l.: Anne Goldthwaite

GOYA Y LUCIENTES, FRANCISCO JOSÉ DE (Spanish 1746–1828)

EVIL COUNSEL   *Plate 9a*
ink wash drawing 10 × 6¾, *c.* 1805, *unsigned, inscribed* in pencil, l.c.: "cuidado con los consejos"
Collections: M. A. Beurdeley, Paris
References: Paul Lafond "Goya", p. 157, no. 89; A. L. Mayer "Francisco

de Goya", cat. no. 642; Beurdeley Sale Cat., Galerie Georges Petit, June 1920, illus.
Exhibited: Albright Art Gallery, Buffalo, October 1923; Institute of Fine Arts, New York University, Goya Exh. (at Wildenstein & Co.), November 9–December 16, 1950, no. 56

THE REPENTANT PETER   *Plate 6*
canvas 29×25½, *painted c.* 1824–25, *signed* l.r.c.: Goya
Collections: Don A. Pidal, Madrid; Duc de Trévise, Paris
References: A. de Beruete y Moret "Goya", vol. II, pp. 138–39; A. L. Mayer "Goya", no. 68, p. 172; V. von Loga "Francisco de Goya", no. 53; A. F. Calvert "Goya", pl. 268; S. Calleja, Goya Catalogue, pl. 215; A. L. Mayer "A Late Goya", Burlington Magazine, September 1937, p. 139, illus. p. 138; José Gudiol "Spain's Goya", Art News, February 15, 1941, p. 11
Exhibited: New York World's Fair, "Masterpieces of Art", 1939, no. 154; Art Institute of Chicago "The Art of Goya", January–March 1941, no. 158, illus. p. 88 of cat. with text; Institute of Fine Arts, New York University, Goya Exh. (at Wildenstein & Co.), November 9–December 16, 1950, no. 46, illus. in cat.

GRAHAM, JOHN DABROVSKI (Russian-American Contemporary)

BLIND BEGGAR
canvas 35½×29¾, *signed* u.l.: Graham, Paris /28

DR. CLARIBEL CONE
pencil drawing on tan paper 14×10⅛, *signed and inscribed* l.l.: Dr. Claribel Cone by Graham

FLOWERS IN PINK VASE
canvas 21×17, *signed* l.l.: Graham /28

HARLEQUIN AND HEAVY HORSES
canvas 18×22, *signed* l.l.: Graham 27

THE IRON HORSE
canvas 20×28, *signed* l.r.: Graham 27

THE LONELY ROAD
canvas 21¾×15, *signed* l.l.: Graham /28

GRANT, DUNCAN (English Contemporary)

> *LANDSCAPE WITH BRIDGE*
> canvas-board 10½ × 13¾, *signed* l.l.: D. G. 1921

EL GRECO (Domenikos Theotokopoulos) (Greek *c.* 1541–1614)

> *THE REPENTANT PETER*   *Plate 3*
> canvas 37 × 30, *painted c.* 1600, *signed* l.l.: Domenikos Theotokopoulos
> *Collections:* Ignacio Zuloaga; Ivan Tschoukine, Paris; Heilbuth Collection
> *References:* Cossio "El Greco" (1908), p. 601, no. 316; Mayer "El Greco",
> (1926), no. 208; Heilbuth Collection Catalogue, no. 42, p. 67
> *Exhibited:* Albright Art Gallery, Buffalo, 1931; Brooklyn Museum, 1935;
> Smith College Museum of Art, 1937

GRIFFIN, WALTER (American 1861–1935)

> *CARCASSONNE*
> composition panel 13 × 16, *signed* l.l.: Griffin

GRIS, JUAN (Spanish 1887–1927, School of Paris)

> *ABSTRACTION*   *Plate 159a*
> cardboard panel 11¼ × 7⅝, *signed* u.l.: Juan Gris 1915; *inscribed* l.l.: A
> mon ami André Salmon souvenir affectueux Juan Gris 8–19
> *Exhibited:* Cincinnati Modern Art Society, Juan Gris Exh., 1948, no. 12,
> illus. in cat.

> *BOWL AND PACKAGE OF CIGARETTES*   *Plate 159b*
> canvas 13 × 16, *signed* l.r.: Juan Gris 23
> *Collections:* Albert Flechtheim, Berlin; Walter P. Chrysler, Jr.
> *Exhibited:* Cincinnati Modern Art Society, Juan Gris Exh., 1948, no. 52

> *STILL LIFE WITH NEWSPAPER*   *Plate 158*
> canvas 28¾ × 23⅝, *signed* l.l.: Juan Gris 8–16
> *Collections:* Miss Katherine S. Dreier
> *References:* E. Tériade "Juan Gris", Cahiers d'Art (no. 5–6, 1928),
> illus. p. 237

GROMAIRE, MARCEL (French Contemporary)

THE EDGE OF THE FOREST
canvas $31\frac{7}{8} \times 39\frac{3}{8}$, *signed* l.r.: Gromaire 1948

GROPPER, WILLIAM (American Contemporary)

PRETZEL VENDOR
canvas $15 \times 18\frac{1}{4}$, *signed* l.r.: Gropper 39

REFUGEES
canvas 18×30, *painted* 1939, *signed* l.r.: Gropper

GROSZ, GEORGE (German-American Contemporary)

LANDSCAPE IN BAYSIDE
watercolor $5\frac{1}{4} \times 8\frac{1}{4}$, *signed* l.r.: Grosz 35

STREET IN HARLEM
watercolor 23×16, *signed* l.r.: Grosz

THE SURVIVOR
ink drawing $22\frac{1}{2} \times 17\frac{3}{4}$, *signed* l.r.: Grosz 1925

GUARDI, FRANCESCO (Italian 1712–1793)

PIAZZA SAN MARCO
sepia pen and wash drawing $5 \times 8\frac{7}{8}$, *unsigned*
Collections: Paul Richter; David Weill, Paris

Plate 4a

GUYS, CONSTANTIN (French 1805–1892)

THE TEAM (L'Attelage)
sepia pen and wash drawing $4\frac{1}{4} \times 6\frac{1}{8}$, *unsigned*

A FASHIONABLE WOMAN (Une Élégante)
watercolor drawing $13\frac{1}{2} \times 9\frac{1}{4}$, *unsigned*

46

YOUNG SPANISH GIRL (Jeune Fille Espagnole)   Plate 9b
watercolor and pencil drawing 7×6, *unsigned*

VANITY FAIR (La Promenade)   Plate 28
watercolor and pen drawing 12½×16, *unsigned*
Collections: Dikran Kélékian

HALE, LILLIAN WESTCOTT (American Contemporary)

HOME LESSONS
canvas 46×40, *signed*

HALPERT, SAMUEL (American 1884–1930)

PONT NEUF
canvas 25¾×32, *signed* l.r.: S. Halpert 25

THROUGH THE WINDOW
canvas 20×16, *signed* l.r.: S. Halpert 18

HAN DYNASTY BRICK

WHITE TERRA COTTA FUNERAL BRICK
6½ in. high by 17½ in. long by 3 in. thick, tongued and grooved. Low
relief carving. Chinese, Han Dynasty (206 B.C.–A.D. 220)

HARTL, LEON (American Contemporary)

DAIRY FARM
wood panel 18×26, *signed* l.l.: Leon Hartl 36

HARTLEY, MARSDEN (American 1878–1943)*

AFTER SNOW
canvas-board 12×12, *painted c.* 1916, *signed* l.l.c.: Marsden Hartley

GARDENER'S GLOVES AND SHEARS
canvas-board 16×20, *unsigned*

47

OFF TO THE BANKS   *Plate 184b*
canvas-board 11¾ × 15¾, *unsigned*

OFF TO THE BANKS AT NIGHT
masonite panel 30 × 40, *signed* l.r.: M. H. '42

SEA VIEW, NEW ENGLAND
canvas-board 12 × 16, *painted 1934, signed* l.c.: M. H.

WILD ROSES   *Plate 187*
masonite panel 22 × 28, *painted 1942, unsigned*
Exhibited: Walker Art Center, Minneapolis, 1943; Museum of Modern
Art, Feininger-Hartley Exh., 1944, illus. in cat., p. 89; Tate Gallery,
London, Exh. of American Paintings, 1946

WOOD LOT, MAINE WOODS
canvas-board 28 × 22, *painted 1938, signed* l.l.c.: M. H.
Exhibited: Stedelijk Museum, Amsterdam, 1950

HASSAM, CHILDE (American 1859–1935)

NOON ON THE ROCKS
canvas mounted on composition panel 13 × 25, *signed* l.l.c.: Childe
Hassam 1918

WASHINGTON ARCH, SPRING   *Plate 81*
canvas 26 × 21½, *signed* l.r.: Childe Hassam 1890

HENRI, ROBERT (American 1865–1929)

LITTLE DUTCH GIRL
canvas 24 × 20, *signed* l.l.c.: Robert Henri
Exhibited: American Federation of Arts' Traveling Exh. of "The Eight",
1940–41

HERRMANN, FRANK (American 1866–1942)

NEW YORK, STORMY DAY
cardboard panel 15 × 24, *unsigned*

48

HICKS, REV. EDWARD (American 1780–1849)

THE PEACEABLE KINGDOM   *Plate 12*
canvas 24×31¾, *painted 1846, unsigned, inscribed* on stretcher: Painted by
Edward Hicks in the 66th year of his age

HOFER, KARL (German Contemporary)

PEACHES
canvas 16×24, *signed* u.r.: K.H. 38

HOGARTH, WILLIAM (English 1697–1764)

THE SINGING PARTY   *Plate 4b*
canvas 28½×36¼, *unsigned*
Collections: Duke of Vernon and heirs

HOMER, WINSLOW (American 1836–1910)

GIRL WITH PITCHFORK
canvas 24×10½, *signed* l.r.: W. H. 1867
Collections: Mrs. Charles Savage Homer
References: Lloyd Goodrich "Winslow Homer" (1944)
Exhibited: Addison Gallery, Phillips Academy, Andover

ROWING HOME   *Plate 45a*
watercolor 13½×19½, *signed* l.l.: Homer 1890
Collections: J. Alden Weir
References: Lloyd Goodrich "Winslow Homer"; Wm. H. Downes "The
Life and Works of Winslow Homer", illus.
Exhibited: Museum of Modern Art, Homer-Ryder-Eakins Exh., May
1930, no. 28, illus. in cat.; Museum of Modern Art, American Exh.,
1932; Whitney Museum of American Art, Homer Centenary Exh.,
December 1936–January 1937, no. 66; Columbus Gallery of Fine Arts,
1937; Carnegie Institute, Homer Centenary, January–March 1937, no.
120

TO THE RESCUE Plate *44*
canvas 24 × 30, *painted* 1882, *signed* l.l.: Homer
References: Lloyd Goodrich "Winslow Homer"; Wm. H. Downes "The
Life and Works of Winslow Homer", illus. opp. p. 150
Collections: Thomas L. Manson, Jr.
Exhibited: Art Institute of Chicago, 1923; Museum of Modern Art,
Homer-Ryder-Eakins Exh., 1930, no. 7; Baltimore Museum of Art,
1932; Carnegie Institute, Homer Centenary Exh., 1937, no. 12

HOPPER, EDWARD (American Contemporary)

APPROACHING A CITY Plate *197*
canvas 27 × 36, painted 1946, *signed* l.r.c.: Edward Hopper
Exhibited: Baltimore Museum of Art "Themes and Variations in Painting
and Sculpture", 1948, no. 124; Whitney Museum of American Art,
Hopper Retrospective Exh., February–March 1950, no. 32, illus. in cat.

SANTA FÉ, NEW MEXICO
watercolor 13½ × 19½, *signed* l.l.: Edward Hopper, Santa Fé 1925

SUNDAY
canvas 29 × 34, *painted* 1926, *signed* l.r.: Edward Hopper
Exhibited: Museum of Modern Art, "Edward Hopper", November 1933,
no. 2, illus. in cat.; Carnegie Institute, "Edward Hopper", March–April
1937, no. 22; Hopper Retrospective Exh., Whitney Museum of American
Art; Museum of Fine Arts, Boston; Detroit Institute of Arts, 1950, no. 19
in cat.

HUTSON, CHARLES W. (American 1840–1936)

SECRET PASSAGE TO THE SWAMPS
academy board panel 24 × 18, *signed* l.r.: C. H.

INGRES, JEAN AUGUSTE DOMINIQUE (French 1780–1867)

BATHER (La Petite Baigneuse) Plate *14*
canvas 12¾ × 9¾, *signed* l.r.: Ingres 1826
References: Charles Blanc "Ingres, sa vie et ses oeuvres" (1870), p. 232;
Henry Lapauze "Ingres" (1911), p. 226

50

Collections: Baron Moure, Sr., Paris, 1830; Baron Moure, Jr.; Baron François de Hatvany, 1911

Exhibited: Galerie Georges Petit "Ingres", 1911, no. 32; Paul Rosenberg, Paris, "Great Masters of French 19th Century Painting", 1931, no. 47, illus. in cat.

INNESS, GEORGE (American 1825–1894)

GRAY DAY, GOOCHLAND
wood panel 18×24, *signed* l.r.: G. Inness 1884
Collections: Peter W. Rouse

LAKE ALBANO   *Plate 40*
canvas 30×45, *signed* l.l.: Geo. Inness 1869
Collections: S. M. Nickerson, Boston
Exhibited: Museum of Modern Art, 1932; Wadsworth Atheneum, Hartford, 1935; George Walter Vincent Smith Art Museum, Springfield, 1946; Brooklyn Museum, 1946; Corcoran Gallery of Art, 1949

MOONLIGHT, TARPON SPRINGS   *Plate 41*
canvas 30×45, *signed* l.r.: G. Inness 1892

JACOB, MAX (French Contemporary)

CHRIST STILLING THE TEMPEST
gouache 8×10¼, *signed* l.r.: Max Jacob 28

KANDINSKY, WASSILY (Russian 1866–1944)

AUTUMN   *Plate 147*
canvas 23¾×32½, *painted* 1912, *signed* l.r.: Kandinsky

SUCCESSION
canvas 32×39½, *signed* l.l.: K 35

KANE, JOHN (American 1860–1934)

ACROSS THE STRIP
canvas 32¼×34¼, *signed* l.r.: John Kane 1929

51

Exhibited: Carnegie Institute, 29th International Exh., 1930, no. 88; Carnegie Institute, John Kane Memorial Exh., 1936, no. 16

BLOWING BUBBLES
canvas 10 × 12, *painted* 1931, *unsigned*

KANTOR, MORRIS (American Contemporary)

THE BLACK LACE PARASOL
canvas 39½ × 29½, *signed* l.l.: M. Kantor, 1931
Exhibited: Musée du Jeu de Paume, Paris, "Three Centuries of Art in the United States", 1938, no. 102

HOUSE BY THE SEA
canvas 16 × 19, *signed* l.l.: M. Kantor 1930

UNION SQUARE, NIGHT   Plate 215
canvas 33½ × 27, *signed* l.r.: M. Kantor 1928

KARFIOL, BERNARD (American Contemporary)

BOY   Plate 220
canvas 36 × 27, *signed* l.l.: B. Karfiol
Exhibited: Stockholm, Copenhagen, Munich, Exh. of American Art, 1930; Carnegie Institute, "Bernard Karfiol", 1939, no. 1

IN OUR SHACK
canvas 35 × 40, *signed* l.l.: B. Karfiol

WRESTLERS
canvas 12 × 16, *signed* l.r.: B. Karfiol

KELLER, HENRY G. (American 1869–1949)

AUTUMN FRUITS
canvas 31½ × 40, *painted* 1922, *signed* l.r.: H. G. Keller, Spain
Exhibited: Cleveland Museum of Art, Keller Memorial Exh., 1950, no. 31, illus. in cat.

KENT, ROCKWELL (American Contemporary)

BURIAL OF A YOUNG MAN   *Plate 206a*
canvas 28×52, *unsigned*

FATHER AND SON
canvas 28×34, *unsigned*

THE FINDING OF GOLD
brush and pen drawing 7×8½, *signed* l.r.: Rockwell Kent, Alaska

THE ROAD ROLLER
canvas 34×44½, *signed* l.r.: Rockwell Kent 1909
Exhibited: Venice, Exh. of American Painting, 1924; Musée du Jeu de
Paume, Paris, "Three Centuries of Art in the United States", 1938,
no. 105

VOYAGERS
canvas 28×44, *signed* l.l.: Rockwell Kent 1923
Exhibited: Stockholm, Copenhagen, Munich, Exhibition of American
Art, 1930

KLEE, PAUL (Swiss 1879–1940)*

ACTOR OF THE ORIENTAL THEATRE   *Plate 146*
canvas mounted on cardboard 20½×15½, *painted* 1934, *signed* l.l.c.: Klee
References: Karl Nierendorf "Paul Klee, paintings and watercolors, 1913
to 1939", illus. in color
Exhibited: Cincinnati Art Museum, 1942; Philadelphia Art Alliance
"Paul Klee", 1944, no. 46; Minneapolis Institute of Arts, 1948; Traveling
Exhibition of Klee's Works from the Berne Foundation, Switzerland,
and American Collections, 1949–50, no. 69

ARAB SONG   *Plate 149*
oil on burlap 36×25¼, *painted* 1932, *signed* u.r.: Klee
References: Hans Schiess "Notes on Klee", Cahiers d'Art, 5–8, 1934,
illus. p. 183
Exhibited: Philadelphia Art Alliance, Klee Exh., 1944, no. 4; Minneapolis Institute of Arts, 1948; Klee Traveling Exhibition, 1949–50,
no. 60, illus. in cat.

ARRIVAL OF THE CIRCUS   *Plate 148a*
plaster panel $6\frac{3}{4} \times 10\frac{7}{8}$, *painted* 1926, *signed* l.c.: Klee
References: "Paul Klee" (Museum of Modern Art, 1945), illus. p. 27
Exhibited: Klee Traveling Exh., 1949–50, no. 38

BOTANICAL LABORATORY   *Plate 150*
watercolor $14 \times 9\frac{1}{2}$, *painted* 1928, *signed* u.r.: Klee
Exhibited: Arts Club of Chicago, Klee Memorial Exhibition, 1941, no. 67

THE CATHEDRAL
oil on mounted paper $9\frac{1}{2} \times 12\frac{1}{4}$, *painted* 1924, *signed* u.l.: Klee
References: Will Grohmann "Paul Klee", illus. p. 19

EFFLORESCENCE
composition panel $13 \times 10\frac{5}{8}$, *painted* 1937, *signed* u.r.: Klee
Exhibited: Arts Club of Chicago, Klee Memorial Exh., 1941

GARDEN STILL LIFE
watercolor $13\frac{1}{4} \times 9$, *painted* 1924, *signed* l.l.: Klee
Exhibited: Arts Club of Chicago, Klee Memorial Exh., 1941, no. 66;
Philadelphia Art Alliance, "Paul Klee", 1944, no. 38

THE LAND OF LEMONS
watercolor 9×12, *painted* 1929, *signed* l.l.: Klee

PICTURE ALBUM   *Plate 151*
canvas $23\frac{1}{2} \times 22\frac{1}{4}$, *painted* 1937, *signed* l.l.: Klee
References: "Paul Klee" (Museum of Modern Art, 1945), illus. p. 57
Exhibited: Klee Traveling Exhibition, 1949–50, no. 78; University
Gallery, University of Minnesota, 1950; Duke University, 1951

TREE NURSERY
gesso panel $17\frac{1}{4} \times 20\frac{3}{4}$, *signed* u.l.: Klee 29   *Plate 148b*
Exhibited: Philadelphia Art Alliance "Paul Klee", 1944, no. 17; University Gallery, University of Minnesota, 1950; Duke University, 1951

THE WAY TO THE CITADEL
oil on cloth mounted on board $26\frac{1}{4} \times 22\frac{1}{2}$, *painted* 1937, *signed* u.l.: Klee
Exhibited: Philadelphia Art Alliance "Paul Klee", 1944, no. 10; Duke
University, 1951

YOUNG MOE
oil on newspaper mounted on burlap $20\frac{7}{8} \times 27\frac{5}{8}$, *painted* 1938, *signed* l.r.:
Klee
Exhibited: Duke University, 1951

KNATHS, KARL (American Contemporary)*

BAR ROOM
canvas 36×46, *painted c.* 1932, *signed* l.l.: Karl Knaths
Exhibited: Whitney Museum of American Art, "Juliana Force and
American Art", 1949, no. 69

CIN-ZIN
canvas 24×30, *painted* 1945, *signed* l.r.: K. Knaths
Exhibited: Baltimore Museum of Art "Themes and Variations in Painting
and Sculpture", April–May 1948, no. 61, illus. p. 30, with note on the
painting by Duncan Phillips

CLAM DIGGERS
Plate 209

canvas 50×30, *painted c.* 1928–29, *signed* l.r. side: Knaths

COCK AND GLOVE
Plate 208

canvas 36×26, *painted c.* 1927–28, *signed* l.r.: Knaths
References: Duncan Phillips "Karl Knaths", "The Artist Sees Differently",
vol. I, p. 113; Forbes Watson "American Painting Today" (1939), illus.
p. 135; Martha Candler Cheney "Modern Art in America" (1939), p. 74,
pl. 16; Oliver W. Larkin "Art and Life in America" (1949), p. 382
Exhibited: Baltimore Museum of Art, 1940; Art Institute of Chicago
"Karl Knaths", 1942, no. 1, illus. in cat.; Detroit Institute of Arts,
1942; Bennington College, Knaths Exh., 1944

CONNECTICUT CLOCK
Plate 211b

canvas 30×40, *painted* 1949, *signed* l.r.c.: Karl Knaths

CYLINDERS
canvas 30×40, *painted* 1944, *signed* l.r.: Karl Knaths

DEER IN SUNSET
canvas 36×42, *painted* 1946, *signed* l.r.: Karl Knaths

FRIGHTENED DEER IN MOONLIGHT   *Plate 210a*
canvas 36×48, *painted* 1932, *signed* l.r.: Karl Knaths
Exhibited: Art Institute of Chicago, "Karl Knaths", 1942, no. 4

GERANIUM IN NIGHT WINDOW
canvas 24×20, *painted* 1922, *signed* l.r.: Knaths

GREEN SQUASH
canvas 24×27, *painted* 1948, *signed* l.r.: Karl Knaths

HARVEST   *Plate 210b*
canvas 40×48, *painted* 1933, *signed* l.r.: Karl Knaths
Exhibited: Corcoran Gallery of Art, 14th Biennial Exh., 1935; Baltimore
Museum of Art, 1939; Syracuse Museum of Fine Arts, 1939; M. H. De
Young Museum, San Francisco "7 Centuries of Painting", 1940; Art
Institute of Chicago, 51st Annual Exh., 1940; "Karl Knaths", 1942, no.
5; Detroit Institute of Arts, 1942; Art Gallery of Toronto "Contemporary
American Painting", 1945

KIT AND KIN   *Plate 211a*
canvas 40×50, *painted* 1947, *signed* l.r.: Karl Knaths
References: Art News, December 1947, p. 20, illus.

MEXICAN PLATTER
canvas 42×48, *painted* 1946, *signed* u.r.: Karl Knaths
Exhibited: Carnegie Institute, "Painting in the United States, 1947";
Corcoran Gallery of Art "De Gustibus", 1949, no. 59, illus. in cat.

MOONLIGHT, HARBOR TOWN
canvas 34×34, *painted* 1938, *unsigned*
Exhibited: Art Institute of Chicago, "Karl Knaths", 1942, no. 7; Baltimore Museum of Art, Knaths Exh., 1943

THE MOORS
canvas 27×36, *painted* 1947, *signed* l.l.c.: Karl Knaths

ORARIAN
canvas 36×30, *painted* 1941, *signed* l.c.: K. Knaths
Exhibited: Art Institute of Chicago, "Karl Knaths", 1941, no. 9;
Pennsylvania Academy of Fine Arts, 139th Annual Exh., 1943; Baltimore
Museum of Art, Knaths Exh., 1943

RED TABLE
canvas 24×30, *painted* 1929, *signed* l.r.: Knaths
Exhibited: Art Institute of Chicago, "Karl Knaths", 1942, no. 2, illus.
in cat.

UP ALONG
watercolor 15×19½, *painted c.* 1927, *signed* l.r.c.: Knaths

References to many of the above paintings may be found in E. M. Benson
"Karl Knaths", American Magazine of Art, June 1936, pp. 365–75,
illus.; Duncan Phillips "Knaths: Maturity of a Poetic American", Art
News, May 1–14, 1942, pp. 28–29, 40, illus.

KOKOSCHKA, OSKAR (Austrian Contemporary)*

COURMAYEUR   *Plate 202*
canvas 35½×52, *painted* 1927, *signed* l.r.: O. K.
Collections: Marczell von Nemes, Munich
References: Kunst und Dekoration, xxxiv, 1930, illus. in color, p. 82;
Kunst und Kuenstler, xxix, 1931, p. 185; Edith Hoffmann "Kokoschka,
Life and Work" (1947), p. 325, illus. p. 160, no. 217; Paul Westheim:
essay on Kokoschka and "Courmayeur" to accompany Twin Print, No. 59
Exhibited: Leicester Galleries, London, 1928; Kunsthalle, Mannheim,
1931, no. 70; Galerie Georges Petit, Paris, Exposition Kokoschka, 1931,
no. 29; Arts Club of Chicago, 1941; Kokoschka Traveling Exh., 1948–49

LAC D'ANNECY
canvas 29¾×39½, *painted* 1928, *unsigned*
Exhibited: Minneapolis Institute of Arts, 1948

LYON   *Plate 203*
canvas 38×51, *painted* 1927, *signed* l.l.: O. K.
Collections: Mrs. E. Katzenellenbogen
References: Biermann "Kokoschka" (1929), pl. 30; Heilmaier "Koko‑
schka" (1929), pl. 28; Edith Hoffmann "Kokoschka, Life and Work"
(1947) no. 218, p. 325, pl. 49
Exhibited: Cassirer, Berlin, 1927; Leicester Galleries, London, 1928;
Kunsthalle, Mannheim, 1931; Galerie Georges Petit, Paris, 1931; Oester‑
reichisches Museum, Vienna, 1937; Stedelijk Museum, Amsterdam,
1945–46; Kokoschka Traveling Exh., 1948–49

PORTRAIT OF A CARDINAL   *Plate 200*
canvas 39½×28½, *painted 1946, unsigned*

PORTRAIT OF MME. FRANZOS   *Plate 201*
canvas 45×32½, *painted 1909, signed* l.r.: O. K.
References: Edith Hoffmann "Kokoschka, Life and Work", no. 18, p. 291,
illus. opp. p. 28
Exhibited: Hagenbund, Vienna, 1911; Kunsthaus, Zürich, 1927; Arts
Club of Chicago, 1941; City Art Museum, St. Louis "Van Gogh and
Kokoschka", 1942; Kokoschka Traveling Exh., 1948–49; Minneapolis
Institute of Arts, 1948

VIEW OF PRAGUE FROM THE RIVER
canvas 38×52, *painted 1934, signed* l.r.: O. K.
Collections: Lida Palkovská, Prague
References: Edith Hoffmann "Kokoschka, Life and Work", pp. 332–33,
no. 269
Exhibited: Oesterreichisches Museum, Vienna, 1937; Carnegie Institute,
International Exhibition, 1938, no. 342, pl. 26 in cat.; Baltimore Museum
of Art, 1940; City Art Museum, St. Louis "Van Gogh and
Kokoschka", 1942; Dayton Art Institute, 1951

KOPMAN, BENJAMIN (American Contemporary)

BACK YARD
canvas 28×33, *signed* l.r.: Kopman '44

And three lithographs

KROHG, PER (Norwegian Contemporary)

THE BLACKSMITH
wood panel 23¾×28¾, *signed* l.l.: Per Krohg

CABARET
wood panel, 6¼×8⅝, *signed* l.r.: p. Krohg

PORTRAIT OF THE ARTIST
wood panel 28¾×21¼, *signed* l.l.: Per Krohg

KUHN, WALT (American 1880–1949)

BREAD AND KNIFE
canvas 12×15, *signed* l.l.: Walt Kuhn 1934

GIRL AND MIRROR
canvas 24×20, *painted* 1928, *signed* l.r.: Walt Kuhn
Exhibited: Art Institute of Chicago, Century of Progress Exh., 1933,
no. 586

PERFORMER RESTING
canvas 24×20, *signed* l.r.: Walt Kuhn 1929

SHOW GIRL WITH PLUMES
canvas 40×30, *signed* l.r.: Walt Kuhn 1931

TULIP BUDS   *Plate 182b*
canvas 9×12, *signed* l.r.: Walt Kuhn

KUNIYOSHI, YASUO (American Contemporary)

MAINE FAMILY   *Plate 221*
canvas 30×24, *painted c.* 1922, *unsigned*
Exhibited: Whitney Museum of American Art, Kuniyoshi Exh., 1948,
no. 8

THINKING AHEAD
canvas 16×12, *signed* u.r.: Kuniyoshi

And two lithographs

LACHAISE, GASTON (French 1882–1935)

HEAD OF JOHN MARIN
bronze 12¼ in. high, *signed* at back: G. Lachaise 1928

PEACOCKS
bronze 24 in. high, 53 in. long, *signed* on top of base r.: G. Lachaise 1922

SEA LION
bronze 11 in. high, 14½ in. long, *signed* at back r.: G. Lachaise 1917

LA FARGE, JOHN (American 1835–1910)

FIJIAN CHIEFS IN WAR PAINT
watercolor 9½×21, *unsigned*, inscribed l.r.: chiefs and performers in war dance, Fiji, July 1891

LATHROP, WILLIAM L. (American 1859–1938)

THE TOW PATH
canvas 22×25, *signed* l.r.: W. L. Lathrop

LAUTREC, HENRI DE TOULOUSE (French 1864–1901)

THE PAINTER BEFORE HIS SUBJECT
pencil drawing from a sketchbook 5⅝×8⅞, drawn *c.* 1880, *unsigned*
Collections: Séré de Rivières; John Rewald
Exhibited: Pasadena Art Institute, Lautrec Exh., 1951

MISS MAY BELFORT
lithograph 21½×16½, *signed* in pencil l.r.: THLautrec
Delteil no. 119
Exhibited: Pasadena Art Institute, Lautrec Exh., 1951

ARISTIDE BRUANT
lithograph 10⅜×8½, *signed* in pencil l.r.: THLautrec
Delteil no. 34

LA LOGE (FAUST)
lithograph 14×10¼, *unsigned* (rare proof)
Delteil no. 166
Collections: Count Kessler
Exhibited: Pasadena Art Institute, Lautrec Exh., 1951

LAWRENCE, SIR THOMAS (English 1769–1830)

PORTRAIT OF A YOUNG MAN
canvas 30×25 (early), *unsigned*

LAWSON, ERNEST (American 1873–1939)

AFTER RAIN   Plate 121
canvas mounted on panel 25 × 30, *signed* l.l.: E. Lawson
Exhibited: Museum of Modern Art, December 1929

CITY SUBURBS
canvas mounted on panel 24 × 30, *signed* l.r.c.: E. Lawson

HARLEM VALLEY, WINTER
canvas mounted on panel 26¼ × 34, *signed* l.l.: E. Lawson

MAY IN THE MOUNTAINS   Plate 120
canvas mounted on panel 25 × 30, *signed* l.l.: E. Lawson 1919

NEW ENGLAND BIRCHES
canvas mounted on panel 20 × 24, *signed* l.l.: E. Lawson
Exhibited: American Federation of Arts Traveling Exh. of "The Eight",
1940–41

SPRING
canvas mounted on panel 16 × 20, *signed* l.l.: E. Lawson
Exhibited: Stockholm, Copenhagen, Munich, Exh. of American Art,
1930

SPRING MORNING, HIGH BRIDGE
canvas mounted on panel 16 × 20, *signed* l.l.: E. Lawson

SPRING NIGHT, HARLEM RIVER   Plate 119
canvas mounted on panel 25 × 30, *signed* l.l.: E. Lawson 1913
Exhibited: Baltimore Museum of Art, 1924; Museum of Modern Art,
1929; Whitney Museum of American Art, "New York Realists", 1937,
no. 94, illus. in cat.; Tate Gallery, London, Exh. of American Paintings,
1946

SUNSET, HIGH BRIDGE   Plate 118
canvas mounted on panel 20 × 24, *signed* l.r.: E. Lawson
References: Sheldon Cheney "The Story of Modern Art", illus. p. 431
Exhibited: Baltimore Museum of Art, 1934

WINDY DAY, BRONX RIVER
canvas mounted on panel 25 × 30, *signed* l.l.: E. Lawson

LEONID (BERMAN) (French Contemporary)

HORSES IN FRONT OF A CLIFF
canvas 16¼×10¾, *painted* 1925, *signed* l.l.: Leonid B.

SEACOAST
cardboard panel 9½×14¾, *signed* l.l.: Leonid B.

LOCKWOOD, WARD (American Contemporary)

HORSES IN WINTER
watercolor 13¾×19¼, *signed* l.r.: Lockwood

LUKS, GEORGE (American 1867–1933)*

BLUE DEVILS ON FIFTH AVENUE
canvas 38×44, *painted* 1917, *signed* l.l.: George Luks

A COAL TOWN
watercolor 13¾×19¾, *unsigned*
Exhibited: Whitney Museum of American Art "A History of American Watercolor Painting", 1942, no. 159; Latin-American Exh. "Water-color, U.S.A. from 1870 to 1946", 1946, no. 10

OTIS SKINNER AS COL. BRIDAU   Plate 115
canvas 52×44, *painted* 1919, *signed* l.l.: George Luks
Exhibited: Art Institute of Chicago, 1920; Art Gallery of Toronto, 1921; City Art Museum, St. Louis, 1922; Philadelphia Art Alliance, 1923; Rochester Memorial Art Galley, 1924; Albright Art Gallery, 1924; Museum of Modern Art, 1930; Art Institute of Chicago, 1933; Baltimore Museum of Art, 1934; Newark Museum, 1934, Luks Retrospective Exh., no. 20, illus. p. 43; Montclair Art Museum, 1940; Philadelphia Museum of Art "Artists of the Philadelphia Press", 1945

SULKING BOY   Plate 114
canvas 44×34, *painted* 1912, *signed* l.r.: George Luks
References: Walter Pach "Art in America" (1928), pl. 13
Exhibited: Cleveland Museum of Art, 1924; Newark Museum, Luks Retrospective Exh., 1934, no. 28, illus. p. 46; American Federation of Arts Traveling Exh. of "The Eight", 1940–41

TELLING FORTUNES   Plate 116
canvas 20×16, *painted* 1914, *signed* l.r.: George Luks
Exhibited: Newark Museum, Luks Retrospective Exh., 1934, no. 30

VERDUN, FRANCE
watercolor 15½×16, *painted* 1902, *signed* l.l.: George Luks 1902

LURÇAT, JEAN (French Contemporary)

SMYRNA   Plate 252b
canvas 35×46, *painted* 1927, *signed* l.r. side: Lurçat

MAGNASCO, ALESSANDRO (Italian 1667–1749)

THE SHIPWRECK   Plate 5
canvas 30×41, *unsigned*
Exhibited: Springfield Museum of Fine Arts "Alessandro Magnasco"
1938, no. 22; Baltimore Museum of Art "Contrasts in Impressionism"
1942, no. 2

SINGING BIRDS
canvas 25×11¾, *unsigned*
Collections: Robert T. Francis
Exhibited: City Art Museum, St. Louis, "Venetian Painting of the 18th
Century", 1936, no. 25, illus. in cat.; Springfield Museum of Fine Arts
"Alessandro Magnasco", 1938, no. 13

MAILLOL, ARISTIDE (French 1861–1944)

HEAD OF A WOMAN   Plate 152
bronze 13in. high, *signed* l.r. side: M (in circle)

MANET, ÉDOUARD (French 1832–1883)

BALLET ESPAGNOL   Plate 39
canvas 24×36, *signed* l.r.: Ed. Manet 62

Collections: Durand-Ruel private collection, Paris
References: Duncan Phillips "Manet's Ballet Espagnol", "The Artist Sees Differently", vol. 1, pp. 106–09, illus. in color; John Rewald "The History of Impressionism" (1946), illus. p. 66
Exhibited: Martinet, Paris, Manet Exh., 1863; École des Beaux-Arts, Paris, Manet Memorial Exh., no. 12; Musée du Louvre, Paris, Exposition Manet, 1932; Paul Rosenberg, New York "Masterpieces by Manet", no. 2, illus. in cat., December 1946–January 1947; Wildenstein, New York, Manet Exh., 1948; Yale University Art Gallery "19th Century French Paintings", 1950, no. 7, illus. in cat.

BOY WITH FRUIT
watercolor $8\frac{1}{4} \times 4\frac{1}{2}$, *signed* l.r.c.: Manet

MANGRAVITE, PEPPINO (American Contemporary)

THE ADIRONDACKS
canvas 26×37, *unsigned*

ECSTATIC COLT
canvas $24\frac{1}{4} \times 30$, *signed* l.r.: Peppino Mangravite 1928

THE EXILE
canvas 24×20, *unsigned*

MAN RAY (American Contemporary)

THE BLACK TRAY
canvas 18×24, *signed* l.l.: Man Ray 1914

MARCOUSSIS, LOUIS (School of Paris, 1883–1941)

ABSTRACTION (BROWN AND BLACK)
canvas $13 \times 16\frac{1}{4}$, *signed* l.r.: C. Marcoussis 30

ABSTRACTION (PINK AND GREY)
canvas $18 \times 21\frac{3}{4}$, *signed* l.l.: Marcoussis 30

MARIN, JOHN (American Contemporary)*

ADIRONDACKS AT LOWER AUSABLE LAKE
watercolor $14\frac{5}{8} \times 20\frac{1}{8}$, *signed* l.r.: Marin 47
Exhibited: Art Gallery of Toronto, 1949; Biennale Exh., Venice, 1950

BACK OF BEAR MOUNTAIN   Plate 131
watercolor 17×20, *signed* l.l.: Marin 25
References: MacKinley Helm "John Marin" (1948), pp. 56, 59–60, 66
Exhibited: Museum of Modern Art "Paintings by 19 Living Americans",
December 1929–January 1930, no. 64, illus. in cat.; Smith College
Museum of Art 1934; Museum of Modern Art "John Marin", 1936,
no. 69; Philadelphia Art Alliance "Watercolors by John Marin", 1939;
Smith College Museum of Art, "American Watercolors", 1942; Cincin-
nati Art Museum "Six Americans", 1948; Knoedler Galleries "To Honor
Henry McBride", 1949, no. 19

BLACK RIVER VALLEY
watercolor $15\frac{1}{2} \times 18\frac{3}{4}$, *signed* l.l.: Marin 13

BLUE SEA
watercolor $15\frac{1}{4} \times 20\frac{3}{4}$, *signed* l.r.: Marin 45

BRYANT SQUARE   Plate 135
canvas $21\frac{1}{2} \times 26\frac{1}{2}$, *signed* l.r.: Marin 32
Exhibited: Museum of Modern Art, "John Marin", 1936, no. 167;
Cincinnati Modern Art Society "Expressionism", 1941; Art Gallery of
Toronto "Contemporary American Painting", 1945; Tate Gallery,
London, 1946, Exh. of American Paintings; Biennale Exh., Venice, 1950

CAMDEN ACROSS THE BAY
watercolor $17 \times 20\frac{1}{4}$, *signed* l.r.: Marin 22

FIFTH AVENUE AT FORTY-SECOND STREET   Plate 134
canvas $28 \times 36\frac{1}{2}$, *signed* l.r.: Marin 33
References: E. M. Benson "John Marin" (1935), pp. 95–96, illus. p. 93;
Jerome Mellquist "The Emergence of an American Art" (1942), p. 401
Exhibited: Museum of Modern Art "John Marin", 1936, no. 171 illus. in
cat.; Carnegie Institute "A Survey of American Painting", 1940; Santa
Barbara Museum of Art, 1941; Rhode Island School of Design, 1946;
Biennale Exh., Venice, 1950

FISHING SMACK
watercolor $14\frac{1}{4} \times 18$, *signed* l.l.: Marin 28

FOUR-MASTER OFF THE CAPE   Plate 132
watercolor $15\frac{3}{8} \times 21\frac{3}{4}$, *signed* l.r.: Marin 33
Exhibited: Museum of Modern Art "John Marin", 1936, no. 147

FRANCONIA
watercolor 14×18, *signed* l.r.: Marin 27

FROM FLINT ISLE, MAINE, No. 1
watercolor $15 \times 20\frac{3}{8}$, *signed* l.r.: Marin 47

GREY SEA   Plate 129
watercolor $16\frac{1}{2} \times 20\frac{1}{2}$, *signed* l.r.: Marin 24
References: Lloyd Goodrich "American Watercolor and Winslow
Homer" (1945), illus. p. 62
Exhibited: Museum of Modern Art "John Marin", 1936, no. 63; Golden
Gate Exposition, San Francisco, 1940, no. 1406; Walker Art Center,
Minneapolis; Detroit Institute of Arts; Brooklyn Museum; De Young
Memorial Museum, San Francisco: "American Watercolor and Winslow
Homer", 1945; Tate Gallery, London, Exh. of American Paintings,
1946; Baltimore Museum of Art, 1948; Biennale Exh., Venice, 1950

THE HUDSON
watercolor 13×16, *signed* l.r.: Marin 25
Exhibited: Biennale Exh., Venice, 1950

MAINE ISLANDS   Plate 128
watercolor $16\frac{3}{4} \times 20$, *signed* l.r.: Marin 22
References: E. M. Benson "John Marin", pl. 23; Jerome Mellquist "The
Emergence of an American Art", p. 398; Lloyd Goodrich "American
Watercolor and Winslow Homer", illus. p. 60
Exhibited: Museum of Modern Art "Paintings by 19 Living Americans",
1930, no. 62, illus. p. 56 in cat.; Yale University Art Gallery, 1936;
Museum of Modern Art "John Marin", 1936, no. 50, pl. 50; Musée du
Jeu de Paume, Paris, "Three Centuries of Art in the United States", 1938;
Walker Art Center, Minneapolis; Detroit Institute of Arts; Brooklyn
Museum; De Young Memorial Museum, San Francisco: "American
Watercolor and Winslow Homer", 1945; Tate Gallery, London, Exh.
of American Paintings, 1946; Cincinnati Art Museum, 1948; Corcoran
Gallery of Art "De Gustibus", 1949, no. 46; Albertina Museum, Vienna,
Exh. of American Watercolors, 1950

MT. CHOCORUA
watercolor $16\frac{3}{4} \times 21\frac{1}{2}$, *signed* l.r.: Marin 26

NEAR GREAT BARRINGTON   Plate 130
watercolor $15\frac{1}{2} \times 18\frac{3}{4}$, *signed* l.r.: Marin 25
Exhibited: Philadelphia Museum of Art, 1931; Smith College Museum
of Art, 1934; Philadelphia Art Alliance, 1939; Syracuse Museum of Fine
Arts, 1939; Golden Gate Exposition, San Francisco, 1940; Biennale Exh.,
Venice, 1950

STREET CROSSING, NEW YORK
watercolor $26\frac{1}{4} \times 21\frac{3}{4}$, *signed* l.r.: Marin 28
References: E. M. Benson "John Marin, the Man and His Work", p. 79,
pl. 40; Lloyd Goodrich "American Watercolor and Winslow Homer",
illus. p. 64; MacKinley Helm "John Marin", p. 63, pl. 26
Exhibited: Museum of Modern Art "John Marin", 1936, no. 100; Philadelphia Art Alliance, 1939; Walker Art Center, Minneapolis; Detroit
Institute of Arts; Brooklyn Museum; De Young Memorial Museum, San
Francisco: "American Watercolor and Winslow Homer", 1945; "Watercolor, U.S.A.", Traveling Exh. for Latin-America, 1946–47, no. 30,
illus. in cat.; Albertina Museum, Vienna, Exh. of American Watercolors, 1949; Fogg Museum of Art "Modern Painting", 1951

QUODDY HEAD, MAINE COAST   Plate 133
watercolor 15×22, *signed* l.r.: Marin 33
Exhibited: Biennale Exh., Venice, 1950

THE SEA, CAPE SPLIT
canvas 24×29, *signed* l.r.: Marin 39
Exhibited: Pennsylvania Academy of Fine Arts, 1944

SHIP FANTASY
watercolor $24 \times 18\frac{1}{2}$, *signed* l.l.: Marin 28
Exhibited: Smith College Museum of Art, 1934; Philadelphia Art
Alliance, 1939

TUNK MOUNTAINS, AUTUMN, MAINE   Plate 136
canvas 25×30, *signed* l.r.: Marin 45
Exhibited: Carnegie Institute "Painting in the U.S., 1947"; John Herron
Art Institute, Indianapolis, 1948; Columbus Gallery of Fine Arts, 1948;
Toledo Museum of Art, 1948

MARIS, MATTHYS (Dutch 1835–1917) and MONTICELLI

A CORNER OF THE HAGUE
wood panel $7\frac{5}{8} \times 11\frac{3}{4}$, *signed* l.l.: M.M. 60
Collections: Ichabod Williams

THE QUEEN'S ENTRY   *Plate 30*
wood panel $17\frac{1}{2} \times 31\frac{1}{2}$, *unsigned*

MASSON, ANDRÉ (French Contemporary)

WILL-O'-THE-WISP
canvas board $10 \times 12\frac{1}{2}$, *painted* 1942, *signed* l.l.: André Masson

MATISSE, HENRI (French Contemporary)

INTERIOR WITH EGYPTIAN CURTAIN   *Plate 139*
canvas 51×35, *signed* l.r.: Matisse 48
References: Verve, vol. VI, no. 21–22, illus. in color
Exhibited: Musée d'Art Moderne, Paris, "Paintings by Henri Matisse",
1949; Carnegie Institute, Pittsburgh, International Exh., 1950, no. 128,
pl. 13 in cat.

STUDIO, QUAI ST. MICHEL   *Plate 138*
canvas $57\frac{1}{2} \times 45\frac{3}{4}$, *painted* 1916, *unsigned*
Collections: Sir Kenneth Clark, London
References: R. Kawashima "Matisse" (1936), illus.; Albert C. Barnes
"Henri Matisse", pl. 67; R. H. Wilenski "Modern French Painters"
(1940), pp. 258–59, illus. pl. 74; Art News, December 1940, illus.; Walter
Pach "The Art Museum in America" (1948), p. 292, pl. 48
Exhibited: Galerie Georges Petit, Paris, "Henri Matisse", 1931, no. 36;
Museum of Modern Art "Henri Matisse", 1931, no. 35, illus. in cat.;
Philadelphia Museum of Art "Henri Matisse", 1948; Philadelphia
Museum of Art, Diamond Jubilee Exh., November 1950–February 1951,
no. 96, illus. in cat.

MATTSON, HENRY (American Contemporary)

WILD FLOWERS
canvas 21×18, *signed* u.l.: Mattson

MAURER, ALFRED H. (American 1868–1932)

THE FLORENTINES
canvas mounted on plaster-board 26×18, *painted c.* 1929, *unsigned*
Exhibited: Walker Art Center, Minneapolis; Whitney Museum of American Art; and tour: "A. H. Maurer", 1949–51, no. 61, illus. in cat.

THE OLD TREE
canvas mounted on academy board 30×20, *painted c.* 1924, *signed* l.r.: A. H. Maurer
Exhibited: Baltimore Museum of Art, 1927; Walker Art Center, Minneapolis; Whitney Museum of American Art; and tour: "A. H. Maurer", 1949–51, no. 25

STILL LIFE WITH DOILY   *Plate 137*
composition panel $17\frac{3}{4}$×$21\frac{1}{2}$, *painted c.* 1930, *unsigned*
Exhibited: Baltimore Museum of Art, 1945; Walker Art Center, Minneapolis; Whitney Museum of American Art; and tour: "A. H. Maurer", 1949–51, no. 69, illus. in cat.

McCARTER, HENRY (American 1866–1942)

HUDSON RIVER MISTS
(Gift of friends of the artist at the Pennsylvania Academy of Fine Arts)
canvas 28×32, *unsigned*

MÉNARD, RENÉ (French 1862–1930)

GYPSIES AT SUNRISE
canvas 34×49, *signed* l.r.: E. R. Ménard

MERYON, CHARLES (French 1862–1930)

THE MORGUE
etching $8\frac{3}{8}$×$7\frac{1}{2}$, *signed* on plate l.l.: C. Meryon del. sculp. mdcccliv
Delteil no. 36

NOTRE DAME
etching $10\frac{1}{8}$×$7\frac{1}{4}$, *signed* on plate u.r.: C. M.
Delteil no. 24

MILLER, KENNETH HAYES (American Contemporary)

APPARITION
canvas 25½×22½, *painted* 1911–16, *signed* l.r.c.: K. Hayes Miller

CONSULTING THE CARDS
canvas 24×20, *signed* u.c.: Hayes Miller '24

PORTRAIT OF ALBERT P. RYDER　　　　　　　　　*Plate 167*
canvas 24×20, *signed* u.r.: Hayes Miller 1913
Exhibited: Museum of Modern Art, December 1929–January 1930;
Museum of Modern Art; and tour: "20th Century Portraits", 1942:
Whitney Museum of American Art, Albert P. Ryder Centenary Exh.,
1947

MIRÓ, JOAN (Spanish Contemporary)

RED SUN　　　　　　　　　*Plate 173*
canvas 36×28, *signed* on back: Miró 1948, Le Soleil Rouge

MODIGLIANI, AMEDEO (Italian 1884–1920)

ELENA PAVLOWSKI　　　　　　　　　*Plate 165*
canvas 25½×19¼, *signed* l.r.: Modigliani
Collections: Dolovsky, Paris
References: Arthur Pfannstiel "Modigliani", p. 30
Exhibited: Galerie de France, Paris, "Modigliani", 1945, no. 13; Museum
of Modern Art, Modigliani Exh., 1951; Cleveland Museum of Art,
Soutine and Modigliani Exh., 1951

MONDRIAN, PIET (Dutch 1872–1944)

SQUARE COMPOSITION　　　　　　　　　*Plate 144*
canvas 19¼×19¼, *signed* l.r.c.: P M 22–25

MONET, CLAUDE (French 1840–1926)

THE ROAD TO VETHEUIL　　　　　　　　　*Plate 62*
canvas 23×28½, *signed* l.l.: Claude Monet

Collections: Durand-Ruel, Paris
Exhibited: Detroit Institute of Arts "French Impressionist Painting from Manet to Cézanne", 1940; Wilmington Society of Fine Arts "French Painting, 1847–1947", 1948

MONTICELLI, ADOLPHE (French 1824–1886)

AS YOU LIKE IT   *Plate 31*
wood panel 17×29, *signed* l.r.: Monticelli
Exhibited: George Walter Vincent Smith Art Gallery, Springfield, "Adolphe Monticelli", 1941, no. 14

FÊTE CHAMPÊTRE
wood panel 9×13, *signed* l.r.: A. Monticelli
Collections: Sir William Eden

THE HALT
canvas 18×39, *signed* l.l.: Monticelli
Collections: André de Marseille
Exhibited: George Walter Vincent Smith Art Gallery, Springfield, "Adolphe Monticelli", 1941, no. 16

WOODLAND WORSHIP
wood panel 17×25½, *painted c.* 1872, *signed* l.r.: Monticelli
Exhibited: George Walter Vincent Smith Art Gallery, Springfield, "Adolphe Monticelli", 1941, no. 20

MOORE, HENRY (English Contemporary)

FAMILY GROUP   *Plate 226*
bronze 17½ in. high, *signed* on rear of base: Moore '46
References: Charles Seymour, Jr. "Tradition and Experiment in Modern Sculpture" (1949), illus. p. 67

FIGURES IN A SETTING   *Plate 227b*
watercolor, ink and crayon drawing 14¼×20¼, *signed* l.l.: Moore 42
References: Charles Seymour, Jr. "Tradition and Experiment in Modern Sculpture", illus. p. 78, illus. detail, p. 79

MORISOT, BERTHE (French 1841–1895)

> TWO GIRLS *(Les Deux Fillettes)*   Plate 55
> canvas 26×21½, *signed* l.r.: Berthe Morisot
> *Exhibited:* Arts Club of Chicago "Berthe Morisot", 1943, no. 22

MOSES, ANNA MARY R. (GRANDMA)

> HOOSICK FALLS
> masonite panel 19¾×23¾, *signed* l.r.c.: Moses

MUNCH, EDVARD (Norwegian 1863–1944)

> IBSEN IN THE GRAND CAFÉ
> lithograph 16⅞×23¼, *drawn* 1902, *signed* in pencil l.r.: E. Munch

> THE PROCESSION   Plate 96
> canvas 25¾×30, *painted c.* 1896–97, *signed* l.r.: Edv. Munch
> *Exhibited:* Holland, 1897; Germany, 1897; Manes Galeri, Prague, Munch
> Exh., 1905

> SELF PORTRAIT
> lithograph 17¾×12½, *signed* in pencil l.r.: Edvard Munch 1895

> WOMAN BY THE SEA
> color lithograph 14¾×17¾, *signed* in pencil l.r.: Edvard Munch 1899, No. 3

MYERS, JEROME (American 1867–1940)*

> BAND CONCERT NIGHT
> composition panel 13¾×19½, *signed* l.r.: Jerome Myers, N.Y., 1910
> *Exhibited:* Jerome Myers Memorial Exh., Whitney Museum of American
> Art, 1941; Virginia Museum of Fine Arts, Baltimore Museum of Art,
> 1942

> EVENING ON THE PIER
> canvas 19×25, *signed* l.r.: Jerome Myers 1921
> *Exhibited:* American Exh., Budapest, 1930; Biennale Exh., Venice, 1930;
> Jerome Myers Memorial Exh., Whitney Museum of American Art, 1941;
> Virginia Museum of Fine Arts, Baltimore Museum of Art, 1942

LITTLE MOTHER
composition panel 16½×13¼, *signed* l.l.: Jerome Myers 1916

MARKET IN PARIS
canvas 30×25, *signed* l.l.: Jerome Myers 1920
Exhibited: Jerome Myers Memorial Exh., Whitney Museum of American Art, 1941; Virginia Museum of Fine Arts, 1942

NIGHT, SEWARD PARK
canvas 30×25, *signed* l.r.: Jerome Myers 1919
Exhibited: Jerome Myers Memorial Exh., Whitney Museum of American Art, 1941; Virginia Museum of Fine Arts, 1942

RECREATION PIER
canvas mounted on wood 10¼×8, *signed* l.l.: Jerome Myers
Exhibited: Jerome Myers Memorial Exh., Whitney Museum of American Art, 1941; Virginia Museum of Fine Arts, Baltimore Museum of Art, 1942

THE TAMBOURINE   Plate 117
canvas 22×32, *signed* l.l.: Jerome Myers, N.Y., 1905
Exhibited: Whitney Museum of American Art, Jerome Myers Memorial Exh., 1941; Tate Gallery, London, Exh. of American Paintings, 1946

WAITING FOR THE CONCERT
canvas 18×24, *signed* l.r.: Jerome Myers 1921

WONDERLAND
canvas 25×30, *signed* l.l.: Jerome Myers
Exhibited: Virginia Museum of Fine Arts, Jerome Myers Memorial Exh., 1942

And two drawings and two etchings

NASH, PAUL (English 1889–1946)

THE SEA
(Gift of Miss Demarest)
canvas 22×35, *signed* l.r.: Paul Nash 1923

73

NEWMAN, ROBERT LOFTIN (American 1827-1912)

THE LETTER
canvas $17\frac{1}{2} \times 13\frac{1}{4}$, *signed* l.l.: R. L. Newman
References: Marchal E. Landgren "Robert Loftin Newman", American
Magazine of Art, March 1935, illus. p. 138; Oliver W. Larkin "Art and
Life in America" (1949), p. 268, illus. p. 267
Exhibited: Whitney Museum of American Art "Paintings by Robert
Loftin Newman", 1935, no. 6; Knoedler Gallery "Two American
Romantics of the 19th Century", 1939, no. 25; Virginia Museum of Fine
Arts; Baltimore Museum of Art, Newman Memorial Exh., 1942, no. 16,
pl. 3 in cat.

NICHOLSON, BEN (English Contemporary)

STILL LIFE (WINTER) Plate 227a
masonite panel $12\frac{1}{2} \times 22\frac{1}{2}$ on mat $17 \times 26\frac{1}{2}$, *signed* on back:
Ben Nicholson November 3–50

TRENDRINE, CORNWALL (2)
canvas on plywood backing $15 \times 14\frac{1}{2}$, *signed* on back: Ben Nicholson
1947
References: "Ben Nicholson" by Herbert Read (London, 1948), pl. 201

O'KEEFFE, GEORGIA (American Contemporary)

DARK RED LEAVES ON WHITE Plate 199
canvas 32×21, *painted* 1925, *unsigned*
Exhibited: Pennsylvania Academy of Fine Arts, 1945; Carnegie Institute,
Pittsburgh, 1945; Rhode Island School of Design, 1946; Tate Gallery,
London, Exh. of American Paintings, 1946

MY SHANTY, LAKE GEORGE
canvas 20×27, *unsigned*
Exhibited: American Federation of Arts Traveling Exh. "Pioneers of
Modern Art in America", 1946–47

PATTERN OF LEAVES
canvas 22×18, *painted* 1924, *unsigned*

RANCHOS CHURCH
canvas 24×36, *unsigned*
Exhibited: Philadelphia Museum of Art, 1931; Art Institute of Chicago, 1934; Dallas Museum of Fine Arts, 1936; Stedelijk Museum, Amsterdam, Exh. of American Painting, 1950

RED HILLS AND THE SUN
canvas 27×32, *painted 1927, unsigned*

THE WHITE PLACE IN SHADOW   *Plate 204*
canvas 30×24, *painted 1940, unsigned*
Exhibited: Museum of Modern Art, O'Keeffe Retrospective Exh., 1946

OROZCO, JOSÉ CLEMENTE (Mexican 1883-1949)

BANDERA
lithograph 10¼×16¾, *signed* on plate, l.r.: J. C. O., and in pencil l.r.: José Clemente Orozco

THE FRANCISCAN
lithograph 12¼×10⅜, *signed* in pencil l.r.: José Clemente Orozco

REQUIEM
lithograph 12×16, *signed* on plate l.r.: J. C. O., and in pencil l.r.: José Clemente Orozco

OZENFANT, AMÉDÉE (French-American Contemporary)

GROTTO
canvas 55×72, *signed* l.r.: Ozenfant 45
Exhibited: Carnegie Institute "Painting in the United States, 1946"

PALMER, SAMUEL (English 1805-1881)

PELE POINT, LAND'S END
pencil drawing 10½×14¾, *unsigned*

75

PARMIGIANINO, IL, FOLLOWER OF (Italian 1503–1540)
(has been attributed to Nicolò dell' Abate (1512–1571))

LANDSCAPE (ALLEGORY)
canvas 25×32⅞, *unsigned*

PERRINE, VAN DEARING (American Contemporary)

MORNING LIGHT
canvas 22×26, *signed* l.l.: Van Perrine

PETO, JOHN FREDERICK (American 1854–1907)

OLD REMINISCENCES
canvas 30×25, *signed* (falsely) l.r.: Wm. Harnett, and *dated* l.l.: 1900
References: Alfred Frankenstein "Harnett, True and False", The Art
Bulletin, March 1949, pp. 40, 41, 42, 44, 45, 46, 48, 50, illus. fig. 6

PHILLIPS, DUNCAN (American Contemporary)*

BARN IN MOUNTAIN VALLEY
(loaned by Marjorie Phillips)
canvas 28×22, *painted* 1950, *signed* l.l.: P

PHILLIPS, MARJORIE (American Contemporary)

AFTER AN AIR RAID
canvas 25×36, *painted* 1944–45, *signed* l.l.: Marjorie Phillips
Exhibited: Santa Barbara Museum of Art, 1945; Tate Gallery, London,
Exh. of American Paintings, 1946; Carnegie Institute, Pittsburgh, 1948

COUNTERPOINT
canvas 25×43, *painted* 1950, *signed* l.l.: Marjorie Phillips 50
Exhibited: California Palace of the Legion of Honor, 1950

BLUE HYACINTHS
canvas 28×18, *signed* l.r.: Marjorie Phillips
Exhibited: Corcoran Gallery of Art, Biennial Exh., 1941; American
British Art Center, 1941; Santa Barbara Museum of Art, 1945

FARM ROAD   Plate 223b
canvas 18×24, *painted* 1943, *signed* l.l.: Marjorie Phillips
Exhibited: Carnegie Institute, Pittsburgh, 1944; Pennsylvania Academy
of Fine Arts, 1945; Santa Barbara Museum of Art, 1945

IN THE ALLEGHENIES
canvas 16×30, *unsigned*
Exhibited: Cleveland Museum of Art, 1925

LITTLE BOUQUET   Plate 223a
canvas 15⅝×14⅛, *signed* l.l.: Marjorie Phillips
Exhibited: Musée du Jeu de Paume, Paris, "Three Centuries of Art in the
United States", no. 132; Bennington College, 1944; Santa Barbara
Museum of Art, 1945

MAYPOLE
canvas 26×34, *signed* l.l.: Marjorie Phillips

MORNING WALK
canvas 24×34, *signed* l.l.: Marjorie Phillips
Exhibited: Baltimore Museum of Art, 1934; Golden Gate International
Exposition, San Francisco, 1940; Bennington College, 1944; Santa
Barbara Museum of Art, 1945

THE OLD BEECH TREE
canvas 24×32, *painted* 1947, *unsigned*

THE OPEN ROAD
canvas 24×34, *unsigned*
Exhibited: Whitney Museum of American Art, 1932; New York World's
Fair, Exh. of American Art, 1939; Santa Barbara Museum of Art, 1941;
Fine Arts Gallery, San Diego, 1941; Akron Art Institute, 1946

POPPIES   Plate 222
canvas board 24×18, *signed* l.r.: Marjorie Phillips
Exhibited: Museum of Modern Art, 1930; Carnegie Institute, Pittsburgh,
International Exh., 1930, no. 34, pl. 36 in cat.; Art Institute of Chicago,
1931; Bennington College, 1944

RICH EARTH
canvas 16×20, *signed* l.r.: Marjorie Phillips

77

RUE DE LA BOETIE
composition panel 9×12, *painted* 1922, *unsigned*

SUN AFTER RAIN   Plate 224
canvas 26×35, *painted* 1948, *unsigned*
Exhibited: Corcoran Gallery of Art, Biennial Exh., 1949; Carnegie Institute, Pittsburgh, "Painting in the United States 1949"

WHITE TULIPS
canvas 26×21, *painted* 1947, *signed* l.l.: Marjorie Phillips
Exhibited: Toledo Museum of Art, 1948; San Francisco Museum of Art, 1949

ZINNIAS
canvas 16×13, *painted* 1947, *signed* l.l.: Marjorie Phillips

PICASSO, PABLO (Spanish Contemporary, School of Paris)

ABSTRACTION   Plate 163b
canvas 14×10¾, *signed* l.l.: Picasso, Biarritz, 1918
Exhibited: Museum of Modern Art, "Painting in Paris", 1930, no. 69

THE BLUE ROOM (La Toilette)   Plate 162
canvas 20×24½, *painted* 1901, *signed* l.l.: Picasso
Collections: Etienne Bignou; Reid, London
References: Christian Zervos "Pablo Picasso" (1932), vol. I, no. 103, illus. p. 51; Alfred H. Barr, Jr., "Picasso, Fifty Years of His Art" (1946), p. 22, illus.
Exhibited: Galerie Berthe Weill, Paris, Picasso Exh., 1902; Art Institute of Chicago, Century of Progress Exhibition, 1933, no. 399, illus. in cat.; Jacques Seligmann, New York, 1936, Picasso Exh., "Blue" and "Rose" Periods, no. 4, illus.; "Picasso, Forty Years of His Art", Museum of Modern Art, 1939; Art Institute of Chicago, 1940; Knoedler Galleries "Picasso before 1907", 1947, no. 6, illus. in cat.

BULL FIGHT   Plate 176
canvas 19¾×25¾, *signed* l.l.: Picasso, Boisgeloup, 27 Juillet XXXIV
Exhibited: "Picasso, Forty Years of His Art", 1939–40, Museum of Modern Art; Art Institute of Chicago; Institute of Contemporary Art, Boston, no. 263, illus. in cat.

THE JESTER   *Plate 163a*
bronze 16 in. high, *executed* 1905, *unsigned*
Collections: Alfred Flechtheim
References: Christian Zervos "Pablo Picasso" (1932), no. 322, illus.
p. 148; Alfred H. Barr, Jr. "Picasso, Fifty Years of His Art" (1946),
p. 38, illus.
Exhibited: Museum of Modern Art, 1939; Art Institute of Chicago, 1940;
Institute of Contemporary Art, Boston, 1940: "Picasso, Forty Years of
His Art"; Watkins Gallery, The American University, Washington
D.C., 1949

STUDIO CORNER
watercolor 8×10¼, *signed* l.l.: 9/1/21 Picasso
Exhibited: Art Institute of Chicago, 16th International Watercolor Exh.,
1937

And two lithographs and two etchings

PIPPIN, HORACE (American 1888–1946)

BARRACKS   *Plate 192b*
canvas 25×30, *painted* 1945, *signed* l.r.: H. Pippin
References: Selden Rodman "Horace Pippin" (1947), no. 85, pl. 35, ref.
pp. 22–23
Exhibited: Corcoran Gallery of Art, Biennial Exhibition, 1945; Phila⁄
delphia Art Alliance, 1947

DOMINO PLAYERS   *Plate 192a*
composition panel 12¾×22, *signed* l.r.: H. Pippin 1943
References: Selden Rodman "Horace Pippin" (1947), no. 69, illus. in
color, ref. p. 19
Exhibited: Philadelphia Art Alliance, 1947

PISSARRO, CAMILLE (French 1831–1903)

PORTRAIT OF CÉZANNE
etching 10⅝×8½, *signed* on plate u.l.: C. Pissarro, and on plate l.r.:
1874 Pissarro

PITTMAN, HOBSON (American Contemporary)

CONVALESCENCE
watercolor $16\frac{3}{4} \times 22\frac{3}{4}$, *signed* l.r.: Hobson Pittman

NINE P.M.
canvas 16×22, *signed* l.l.: Hobson Pittman

Plate 234

WINTER AND ROSES
canvas 27×34, *signed* l.l.: Hobson Pittman

POE, ELISABETH (American 1888–1947)*

AGATE HEIGHTS   *Plate 193a*
watercolor $9\frac{3}{4} \times 13\frac{1}{2}$, *signed* twice l.l.: E. Poe 1938 and E. E. Poe 1938

IN TIME'S YESTERDAY
watercolor $19\frac{1}{2} \times 26$, *signed* l.l.: Elisabeth E. Poe 1939

LONELINESS UNBROKEN
watercolor 9×12, *signed* l.r.: Elisabeth E. Poe 1935

NEW ENGLAND HURRICANE
watercolor $8\frac{1}{2} \times 11\frac{1}{2}$, *signed* l.r.: Elisabeth E. Poe 1937

SANCTUARY
watercolor $8\frac{1}{2} \times 11\frac{1}{2}$, *painted* 1939, *unsigned*

WHERE KINGS REIGNED
watercolor $9 \times 11\frac{1}{2}$, *painted* 1942, *unsigned*

POOR, HENRY VARNUM (American Contemporary)

DEAD CROW
masonite panel 16×20, *painted* c. 1944, *signed* u.l.: H. V. Poor

COLORADO LANDSCAPE
watercolor 14×19, *signed* l.r.: H. V. Poor

PRENDERGAST, CHARLES (American Contemporary)

SCREEN
three-panel wood screen, painted and gilded, *executed* 1916–17

PRENDERGAST, MAURICE (American 1859–1924)*

AFTERNOON, PINCIAN HILL   Plate 82
watercolor 21 × 27, *signed* l.r.: Pincian Hill, Rome, 1898, Prendergast
References: Duncan Phillips "Maurice Prendergast", The Arts, March 1924, illus. p. 131; Margaret Breuning "Maurice Prendergast" (1931), illus.
Exhibited: Museum of Modern Art, November 1932–February 1933; Whitney Museum of American Art, Prendergast Memorial Exh., 1934, no. 13; Cleveland Museum of Art "American Painting from 1860", 1937, illus. in cat.; Addison Gallery of American Art, Phillips Academy, Andover, "The Prendergasts", 1938, no. 15; Tate Gallery, London, Exh. of American Paintings, 1946

AUTUMN FESTIVAL   Plate 85
canvas 24 × 28, *painted* 1917–18, *signed* l.r.: Prendergast
References: Duncan Phillips "Maurice Prendergast", The Arts, March 1924, illus. p. 126, ref. p. 129; Margaret Breuning "Maurice Prendergast" (1931), illus.
Exhibited: Whitney Museum of American Art, Prendergast Memorial Exh., 1934, no. 108; Tate Gallery, London, Exh. of American Paintings, 1946

BLUE SEA
watercolor $14\frac{1}{2} \times 21\frac{1}{2}$, *painted c.* 1914, *signed* l.l.: Prendergast

FANTASY
canvas 21 × 32, *painted c.* 1917, *signed* l.r.c.: Prendergast
References: Duncan Phillips "Maurice Prendergast", The Arts, March 1924, illus. p. 127
Exhibited: Baltimore Museum of Art, 1924; Dallas Museum of Fine Arts "200 Years of American Painting", 1946, no. 18, illus.; American Federation of Arts, Traveling Exh. of "The Eight", 1940–41

LUXEMBOURG GARDENS
wood panel $10\frac{1}{4} \times 13\frac{3}{4}$, *signed* l.l.: Prendergast

NEAR NAHANT
canvas 20×28, *signed* l.l.: Prendergast
Exhibited: American Exh., Budapest, 1930; Biennale Exh., Venice, 1930

PICNIC PARTY
canvas 18×28, *signed* l.l.c.: Prendergast

PONTE DELLA PAGLIA   *Plate 83*
canvas 28×23, *painted* 1899, *signed* l.l.: Prendergast
References: Duncan Phillips "Maurice Prendergast", The Arts, March
1924, illus. opp. p. 125; Margaret Breuning "Maurice Prendergast" (1931),
illus.; John Walker and Macgill James "American Painting from Smibert
to Bellows" (1943), pl. 94
Exhibited: Exh. of American Painting, Venice, 1924; Museum of Modern
Art, November 1932–February 1933; Baltimore Museum of Art, 1934;
Virginia Museum of Fine Arts, 1936; Musée du Jeu de Paume, Paris,
"Three Centuries of Art in the U.S.", 1938; Addison Gallery of
American Art, Phillips Academy, Andover, "The Prendergasts", 1938,
no. 67; Carnegie Institute, Pittsburgh, "Survey of American Painting",
1940, no. 224, pl. 69 in cat.; Brooklyn Museum "The Eight", November
1943–January 1944, no. 45; Museum of Modern Art Traveling Exh. of
"The Eight", 1944; Tate Gallery, London, Exh. of American Paintings,
1946; Corcoran Gallery of Art, "De Gustibus", 1949, no. 34

SNOW IN APRIL   *Plate 84*
canvas 20×28, *painted* 1907, *signed* l.r.: Prendergast
Exhibited: Brooklyn Museum "The Eight", November 1943–January
1944, no. 52

UNDER THE TREES
canvas 24×32, *signed* l.l.: Prendergast
References: Duncan Phillips "Maurice Prendergast", The Arts, March
1924, illus. p. 129

PUVIS DE CHAVANNES, PIERRE (French 1824–1898)

MARSEILLES, PORT OF THE ORIENT   *Plate 37*
canvas 38¾×57½, *painted* 1868, *unsigned*
Collections: Durand-Ruel, Paris; Baron Denys Cochin, Paris; Meyer
Goodfriend, New York

References: Goodfriend Collection Sale Catalogue, 1923 (American Art Association), no. 122, illus.; Will Hutchins "Two Composition Sketches by Puvis de Chavannes", Art and Understanding, March 1930, pp. 230–39, illus. p. 236
Exhibited: Century Club, New York, 1936; Wilmington Society of the Fine Arts, 1948

GREEK COLONY, MASSILIA   Plate 36
canvas 38¾×57½, *painted* 1868, *unsigned*
Collections: Durand-Ruel, Paris; Baron Denys Cochin, Paris; Meyer Goodfriend, New York
References: Goodfriend Collection Sale Catalogue, 1923, no. 121, illus.; Will Hutchins "Two Composition Sketches by Puvis de Chavannes", Art and Understanding, March 1930, pp. 230–39, illus. p. 235
Exhibited: Century Club, New York, 1936; Wilmington Society of the Fine Arts, 1948

SACRED GROVE
watercolor 7½×7½, *signed* l.r.: P. P. Ch.

THE WINE PRESS
canvas 18×13, *signed* l.l.: P. Puvis de Chavannes
Collections: Catholina Lambert; Charles H. Tweed
Exhibited: Baltimore Museum of Art, November 1934–January 1935; Carnegie Institute, Pittsburgh, 1936

RATTNER, ABRAHAM (American Contemporary)

THE SUN
canvas 39⅜×31⅞, *painted* 1943, *signed* l.r.: Rattner

WINDOW AT MONTAUK POINT
canvas 25⅝×31⅞, painted 1943, *signed* l.l.: Rattner

REDON, ODILON (French 1840–1916)

MYSTERY (Mystère)   Plate 61
canvas 29×21½, *signed* l.r.: Odilon Redon
Exhibited: Arts Club of Chicago "Origins of Modern Art", 1940

RENOIR, PIERRE AUGUSTE (French 1841–1919)

THE JUDGMENT OF PARIS   *Plate 72*
sanguine and white chalk drawing $18\frac{5}{8} \times 24\frac{1}{8}$, *executed c.*
1908–10, *signed* l.r.: Renoir
Collections: The artist's son, Pierre Renoir
Exhibited: Museum of Modern Art "Modern Drawings", 1944, illus. p.
24 in cat.; California Palace of the Legion of Honor, Exh. of French
Drawings 1947; Philadelphia Museum of Art "Masterpieces of Drawing", Diamond Jubilee Exh., Nov. 1950–Feb. 1951, no. 105, illus. in cat.

THE LUNCHEON OF THE BOATING PARTY   *Color Repr. and*
   (Le Déjeuner des Canotiers)   *Plate 63*
canvas 51×68, *signed*: Renoir 1881
Collections: Durand-Ruel Private Collection, Paris
References: R. Muther "History of Modern Painting" (1907), vol. III,
p. 125, illus.; J. Meier-Graefe "Renoir" (1912 Fr. trans.), p. 106, illus.;
Georges Rivère "Renoir et Ses Amis" (1921), pp. 186–87, illus. p. 140;
P. Jamot "Renoir" Gazette des Beaux-Arts, December 1923, p. 323,
illus.; Art News, December 8, 1923, illus. p. 22; F. W. (Forbes Watson)
"Le Déjeuner des Canotiers", The Arts, April 1924, p. 203, illus.;
T. Duret "Renoir" (1924), p. 63, illus.; F. Fosca "Masters of Modern
Art", pl. 20; A. Vollard "Renoir" (1925), p. 62, illus.; D. Phillips
"A Collection in the Making" (1926), pp. 34, 107, illus. in color opp.
p. 34; J. Meier-Graefe "Auguste Renoir" (1929), pp. 152–55, no. 137,
illus.; A. André "Renoir" (1930), p. 20, illus.; D. Phillips "The Artist
Sees Differently" (1931), vol. I, p. 19, illus. pl. 51, vol. II; C. Roger-
Marx "Renoir" (1933), p. 91, illus.; Bulletin, Art Institute of Chicago,
April 1933, illus.; Art Digest, May 15, 1933, illus. p. 22; Fine Arts,
June 1933, illus. p. 35; London Studio, August 1933, illus.; W. Groh-
mann "Renoir", Thieme-Becker, XXVIII, 1934, illus. p. 170; A. C.
Barnes and V. De Mazia "The Art of Renoir" (1935), p. 76, 404, illus.;
H. McBride "Renoirs in America", Art News, May 1, 1937, p. 67, illus.;
M. Florisoone "Renoir" (1937), p. 108, illus.; G. Besson "Renoir" (1938),
p. 26, illus.; R. H. Wilenski "Modern French Painters" (1940), p. 47;
W. Uhde "Les Impressionistes", p. 76, illus.; Art News, November 15,
1941, illus. in color, p. 21; Daniel C. Rich "French Impressionism",
Tricolor, August 1944, illus. p. 83; C. L. Watkins "The Language
of Design" (1946), p. 167, illus. p. 166; John Rewald "The History

of Impressionism" (1946), p. 356, illus. opp.; Fiske Kimball and Lionello Venturi "Great Paintings in America" no. 88, p. 190, illus. in color opp.

Exhibited: Les Indépendants, 7th Exh. Paris, 1882, no. 140; Art Institute of Chicago, Century of Progress Exh. 1933, no. 345, illus. in cat.; Century Club, New York, "French Masterpieces" 1936, no. 1, color frontis. of cat.; Cleveland Museum of Art, Great Lakes Exh. 1936, no. 305; Metropolitan Museum of Art, Renoir Exh. 1937, no. 33; Museum of Modern Art, New York, "Art in Our Time", 1939, no. 50, illus. in cat.; "Masterpieces of Art", New York World's Fair, 1940, no. 332, illus. p. 229; Duveen Galleries, New York, Renoir Centennial Exhibition, 1941, No. 36, illus. in cat.

MOTHER AND CHILD (La Maternité)
bronze 21 inches high, *executed c.* 1905, *signed* left side of base: Renoir
References: Charles Seymour, Jr. "Tradition and Experiment in Modern Sculpture" (1949), p. 32, detail illus.
Exhibited: Buchholz Gallery, New York, "Bronzes by Degas, Matisse and Renoir", 1943, no. 29

THE DANCE IN THE COUNTRY
soft-ground etching $8\frac{5}{8} \times 5\frac{3}{8}$, *signed* in ink l.r.: Renoir
References: Delteil no. 2

RICO DI CANDIA, ANDREAS (Cretan 15th–16th Century)

THE PASSION OF THE MADONNA
wood panel $25\frac{1}{4} \times 20\frac{3}{4}$ (Cretan-Byzantine School), *unsigned*
Collections: J. N. Laurvik

ROBINSON, THEODORE (American 1852–1896)

GIVERNY
canvas $15\frac{1}{2} \times 22$, *painted c.* 1889, *unsigned*
References: John I. H. Baur "Theodore Robinson" (1946), no. 89
Exhibited: Newark Museum "American Painting from 1700 to 1900", 1931

TWO IN A BOAT
canvas board 9¾×14, *signed* l.r.: Th. Robinson 1891
References: John I. H. Baur "Theodore Robinson" (1946), no. 229, pl. 22
Exhibited: Society of American Artists, 1895, no. 262; Macbeth Gallery, New York, "Theodore Robinson", 1895, no. 26; Pennsylvania Academy of the Fine Arts, 1895–96, no. 284; The Armory Show, New York, 1913, no. 731; Brooklyn Museum "Theodore Robinson", 1946

ROMANESQUE LIMESTONE HEAD

Limestone sculpture 7 in. high, 12th Century, French, from the church of St. Gilles du Gard, Provence
Collections: Dikran Kélékian

ROSA, SALVATOR (Italian 1615–1673)

ST. FRANCIS IN ECSTASY
canvas 25½×19, *unsigned*
Collections: Mrs. George M. Millard; J. N. Laurvik

ROUAULT, GEORGES (French Contemporary)*

AFTERGLOW, GALILEE (Paysage au bord de la mer)   Plate 141b
canvas 19¾×25½, *painted* before 1930, *signed* l.l.: G. Rouault
References: Lionello Venturi "Georges Rouault" (1940), no. 162, p. 62, pl. 135; James T. Soby "Georges Rouault" (1945), p. 26, illus. p. 81; E. A. Jewell "Rouault" (1945), illus.
Exhibited: Museum of Modern Art, Rouault Exh. 1945, no. 64, illus. in cat.; Grand Rapids Art Gallery, 1947

BOUQUET No. 1
oil and gold leaf on paper mounted on board 13×9½, *painted c.* 1938, *signed* l.r.c.: G. Rouault
Exhibited: Baltimore Museum of Art, 1945; University of Virginia, 1948

BOUQUET No. 2
oil on newspaper 14×10, *painted c.* 1938, *signed* l.r.c.: G. Rouault
References: E. A. Jewell "Rouault", frontis. in color.
Exhibited: University of Virginia, 1948

CHRIST AND THE HIGH PRIEST (Christ et le Docteur)　　　Plate 140
canvas 19½×13½, *painted* before 1937, *signed* u.r.: G. Rouault
References: A Bulletin of the Phillips Memorial Gallery, January 1941,
frontis.; E. A. Jewell "Rouault" (1945), illus.
Exhibited: Rouault Exh., Institute of Contemporary Art, Boston; Phillips
Gallery, Washington; San Francisco Museum of Art, 1940–41, no. 12;
University of Virginia, 1948

CIRCUS TRIO (Clowns)　　　Plate 142
oil on paper mounted on canvas 30×42, *painted c.* 1924,
signed u.r.: G. Rouault
References: Lionello Venturi "Georges Rouault" (1940), p. 59, no. 105,
pl. 84; James T. Soby "Georges Rouault" (1945), p. 21, no. 52, illus.
p. 72; E. A. Jewell "Rouault" (1945), illus.
Exhibited: Rouault Exh., Institute of Contemporary Art, Boston; Phillips
Gallery, Washington; San Francisco Museum of Art, 1940–41, no. 15,
illus. in cat.; Museum of Modern Art "Rouault", 1945, no. 52; Institute
of Contemporary Art, Boston, 1946

STILL WATERS　　　Plate 141a
canvas 9⅞×12¼, *painted* before 1937, *signed* l.r.: G. Rouault
References: E. A. Jewell "Rouault" (1945), illus.

TRAGIC LANDSCAPE
gouache, pastel and ink on paper 18½×23½, *signed* l.l.c.: G. Rouault 1930
Exhibited: Renaissance Society, Chicago, 1933; Smith College Museum
of Art, 1935; Ringling Museum of Art, Sarasota, 1948

VERLAINE　　　*Color Repr. and Plate 143*
canvas 39¾×29⅛, *finished* 1939, *signed* l.r.: G. Rouault
Collections: Vollard, Paris
References: Walter Pach "The Art Museum in America" (1948), p. 292,
pl. 49

SELF PORTRAIT
lithograph 13½×9¾, *signed* on paper, l.r.: Georges Rouault

ROUSSEAU, HENRI (Le Douanier) (French 1844–1910)

NOTRE DAME   *Plate 88*
canvas 13 × 16, *signed* l.r.: H. Rousseau 1909
Collections: Paul Guillaume, Paris
References: Daniel Catton Rich "Henri Rousseau" (1942), p. 58, illus.
p. 61
Exhibitions: Renaissance Society, Chicago, 1933; Museum of Modern Art
"Masters of Popular Painting", 1938, no. 70; Art Institute of Chicago;
Museum of Modern Art "Henri Rousseau", 1942

THE PINK CANDLE (La Bougie Rose)
canvas 6$\frac{3}{8}$ × 8$\frac{3}{4}$, *painted* 1905–08 (?), *signed* l.l.: H. Rousseau
Collections: Mrs. R. A. Workman, London
References: Daniel Catton Rich "Henri Rousseau" (1942), illus. p. 55
Exhibited: Philadelphia Museum of Art "The Post Impressionists", 1935;
Yale University Art Gallery, 1937; Museum of Modern Art "Masters
of Popular Painting", 1938, no. 68, illus. in cat.; Wadsworth Atheneum,
Hartford, 1938; Art Institute of Chicago; Museum of Modern Art
"Henri Rousseau", 1942; Carnegie Institute, Pittsburgh, Rousseau Exh.,
1942; Art Gallery of Toronto, Rousseau Exh., 1943

ROUSSEL, KARL XAVIER (French Contemporary)

FAUN AND NYMPH UNDER A TREE   *Plate 103*
canvas 17 × 23, *signed* l.r.: K. X. Roussel
Exhibited: Carnegie Institute, Pittsburgh, International Exh., 1926

MEDITERRANEAN
composition panel 10$\frac{1}{4}$ × 15$\frac{1}{4}$, *signed* l.l.: K. X. Roussel

RYDER, ALBERT PINKHAM (American 1847–1917)*

DEAD BIRD   *Plate 46a*
wood panel 4$\frac{1}{4}$ × 9$\frac{7}{8}$, *painted* 1890–1900, *unsigned*
Collections: N. E. Montross
References: "Landscape and Figure Painters of America" (1917), pp.
36–37; Frederic Fairchild Sherman "Albert Pinkham Ryder" (1920),

illus.; Frederic Newlin Price "Albert Pinkham Ryder" (1932), no. 26 illus.; John Walker and Macgill James "Great American Paintings from Smibert to Bellows" (1943), illus.
Exhibited: Museum of Modern Art "Homer, Ryder, Eakins", 1930, no. 76; American Exh., 1932–33; "Art in Our Time", 1939, no. 25, illus. in cat.; "Romantic Painting in America", 1943, no. 177, illus. in cat.; Tate Gallery, London, Exh. of American Paintings, 1946; Whitney Museum of American Art, Ryder Centenary Exh., 1947, no. 6

DESDEMONA   *Plate 48*
canvas 14×10, completed 1896, *unsigned*
Collections: Ladd Collection
Exhibited: Whitney Museum of American Art, Ryder Centenary Exh., 1947, no. 7

FISHERMEN'S HUTS   *Plate 49*
canvas 12×14, *signed* l.r.: A. P. Ryder
Collections: N. E. Montross
References: Frederic Newlin Price "Albert Pinkham Ryder" (1932), no. 45
Exhibited: Renaissance Society, Chicago, 1933; Whitney Museum of American Art, Ryder Centenary Exh., 1947, no. 10

GAY HEAD   *Plate 46b*
canvas 8×12½, *signed* l.r.: A. P. Ryder
Collections: Sanden Collection
References: Frederic Newlin Price "Albert Pinkham Ryder" (1932), no. 53, ref. p. 22, illus.
Exhibited: Whitney Museum of American Art, Ryder Centenary Exh., 1947, no. 12

HOMEWARD BOUND   *Plate 45b*
wood panel 9×18, *painted c.* 1893–94, *signed* l.r.: A. P. Ryder
Collections: Frederic Fairchild Sherman
References: Frederic Fairchild Sherman "Albert Pinkham Ryder" (1920), illus.; Frederic Newlin Price "Albert Pinkham Ryder" (1932), no. 61
Exhibited: Museum of Modern Art "Homer, Ryder, Eakins", 1930, no. 80; Dallas Museum of Fine Arts "200 Years of American Painting", 1946, no. 14, illus. in cat.; Whitney Museum of American Art, Ryder Centenary Exh., 1947, no. 14

MACBETH AND THE WITCHES   *Plate 51*

canvas 28¼×35¾, *painted* 1890–1908, *unsigned*
Collections: A. T. Sanden; Haverford College, Haverford, Pa.
References: Frederic Fairchild Sherman "Albert Pinkham Ryder" (1920),
p. 72, no. 103; Frederic Newlin Price "Albert Pinkham Ryder" (1932),
p. 18, no. 90, illus.; Lloyd Goodrich "Albert P. Ryder" (cat. of Ryder
Centenary, Whitney Museum, 1947), pp. 17, 36, illus. p. 32; Richard
Braddock "The Literary World of Albert Pinkham Ryder", Gazette
des Beaux-Arts, January 1948, illus. p. 52; Oliver W. Larkin "Art and
Life in America" (1949), p. 270, illus. p. 269
Exhibited: Metropolitan Museum of Art, 1918, no. 41; Detroit Institute
of Arts, 1929; Museum of Modern Art "Homer, Ryder, Eakins", 1930,
no. 88, illus. in cat.; Kansas City Art Institute, 1933; Lyman Allyn
Museum, New London, Conn., 1934, no. 67; Art Institute of Chicago,
Century of Progress Exh., 1934, no. 403; Cleveland Museum of Art
"American Painting from 1860", 1937, illus. in cat.; Museum of Modern
Art "Modern Masters", 1940, no. 4, illus. p. 14; Carnegie Institute,
Pittsburgh, "Survey of American Painting", 1940, no. 207, illus. pl. 66;
Fogg Art Museum "American Landscape Painting", 1941; Museum
of Modern Art "Romantic Painting in America", no. 178, illus. in cat.;
National Gallery of Art, Washington, 1945–46; Whitney Museum of
American Art, Ryder Centenary Exh., 1947, no. 20, illus. in cat.

MOONLIT COVE   *Plate 47*

canvas 14×17, *painted c.* 1890–1900, *unsigned*
Collections: Mrs. Alexander Morton, New York
References: Frederic Fairchild Sherman "Albert Pinkham Ryder" (1920),
no. 94, p. 71; Frederic Newlin Price "Albert Pinkham Ryder" (1932),
no. 111, illus.; Helen Gardner "Art Through the Ages" (1936), illus.;
Sheldon Cheney "The Story of Modern Art" (1941), p. 424, illus. p. 420
Exhibited: Metropolitan Museum of Art, 1918, no. 34; Museum of
Modern Art "Homer, Ryder, Eakins", 1930, no. 77, illus. in cat.;
American Exh., 1932–33; Art Institute of Chicago, Century of Progress
Exh., 1934, no. 405; Yale University Art Gallery, 1936; Museum of
Modern Art "Art in Progress", 1944, illus. in cat.; Whitney Museum
of American Art, Ryder Centenary Exh., 1947, no. 25, illus. in cat.;
Baltimore Museum of Art "Themes and Variations in Painting and
Sculpture", 1948, no. 116, illus. in cat.; Brooklyn Museum "The Coast
and the Sea", 1948, no. 100

RESURRECTION (Noli Me Tangere)   *Plate 50*
canvas 17×14, *completed* 1885, *unsigned*
Collections: N. E. Montross
References: Frederic Fairchild Sherman "Landscape and Figure Painters of America" (1917), p. 35, illus. opp. p. 36; "Albert Pinkham Ryder" (1920), illus.; Frederic Newlin Price "Albert Pinkham Ryder" (1932), p. 20, no. 141, illus.; Suzanne LaFollette "Art in America" (1929), illus.; Walter Pach "The Art Museum in America (1948), p. 293, pl. 59
Exhibited: Museum of Modern Art "Homer, Ryder, Eakins", 1930, no. 79; Newark Museum Association, 1930–31; Virginia Museum of Fine Arts "Main Currents in the Development of American Painting", 1936, no. 69, illus. in cat.; Golden Gate International Exposition, San Francisco, 1939; Arts Club of Chicago "Origins of Modern Art", 1940; Carnegie Institute, Pittsburgh "Survey of American Painting", 1940, no. 208; Philbrook Art Center, Tulsa, 1945; Arts Club of Chicago, Ryder, Davies Exh., 1946, no. 16; Whitney Museum of American Art, Ryder Centenary Exh., 1947, no. 32, illus. in cat.

SEGONZAC, ANDRÉ DUNOYER DE (French Contemporary)

RIVER LANDSCAPE
canvas 24×32, *signed* l.l.: A. D. de Segonzac
Exhibited: Syracuse Museum of Fine Arts, 1930; Rochester Memorial Art Gallery, 1930; Renaissance Society, Chicago, 1933; Arts Club of Chicago, 1938; University of Virginia, 1948

SEURAT, GEORGES PIERRE (French 1859–1891)

FIRST DRAWING FOR "THE SIDE SHOW" (La Parade)   Plate 74
charcoal or conté crayon drawing 9½×12½, *executed c.* 1882, *unsigned*
References: Germain Seligman "The Drawings of Georges Seurat" (1947), no. 22, illus.
Exhibited: Albright Art Gallery "French Art of the 19th Century", 1932, no. 94; Fogg Art Museum "Style and Technique", 1936, no. 31, illus. in cat.; Jacques Seligmann, New York, "The Stage", 1939, no. 26; American-British Art Center "19th and 20th Century Drawings", 1944; Buchholz Gallery "Seurat, his drawings", 1947, no. 12; Knoedler Galleries, New York, "Seurat", 1949, no. 33, illus. in cat.

THE STONE BREAKER (Le Casseur de Pierres)   *Plate 75*
wood panel 6⅜ × 10, *painted c.* 1884, *signed* l.r.: Seurat
Collections: Félix Fénéon, Paris; Georges Levy, Paris
References: Cahiers d'Art, No. 4, 1931, illus. p. 194
Exhibited: Bernheim-Jeune, Paris, Exposition Georges Seurat, December
1908–January 1909; McLellan Galleries, Glasgow, "A Century of
French Painting", 1927, no. 40; Bignou Gallery, New York, "The Post-
Impressionists", 1940, no. 12

SHAHN, BEN (American Contemporary)

MORNING
tempera on paper mounted on masonite 5¾ × 13¼, *painted* 1943, *signed* l.r.:
Ben Shahn

STILL MUSIC   *Plate 238b*
tempera on cloth mounted on plywood 48 × 83½, *painted* 1948,
signed l.r.: Ben Shahn

And four drawings

SHEELER, CHARLES (American Contemporary)

OFFICES   *Plate 205*
canvas 20 × 13, *signed* l.r.: Sheeler 1922
Exhibited: Stockholm, Copenhagen, Munich, Exh. of American Art,
1930

SICKERT, WALTER RICHARD (English 1860–1942)*

LUDOVICO MAGNO   *Plate 100*
canvas 21½ × 30, *signed* l.r.: Sickert
Collections: Major Frederick Lessore
Exhibited: Carnegie Institute, Pittsburgh, International Exh., 1935, no.
104, illus. in cat.

THE MAKINGS OF AN OMELETTE
canvas 16 × 13, *signed* l.r.: Sickert 1919

PORTE ST. DENIS
canvas 30¼×18½, *signed* l.l.: Sickert
Collections: Major Frederick Lessore, London
Exhibited: Institute of Contemporary Art, Boston, 1946

PORTRAIT OF FRED WINTER   *Plate 80*
canvas 23½×14½, *signed* l.l.: Sickert
Collections: The Art Association of Montreal

VICTORIA AND MELBOURNE   *Plate 95*
canvas 40×41, *signed* l.r.: Sickert

SIDANER, HENRI LE (French 1862–1939)

GIPSY WAGON IN MOONLIGHT
canvas 32×40, *signed* l.r.: Le Sidaner

SISLEY, ALFRED (English 1839–1899)

SNOW AT LOUVECIENNES   *Plate 54*
canvas 22×18, *signed* l.r.: Sisley 74
References: R. H. Wilenski "Modern French Painters" (1940), illus.
opp. p. 31; John Rewald "The History of Impressionism" (1946),
illus. p. 241
Exhibited: Independent Gallery, London, 1928; Detroit Institute of Arts
"French Painting from Manet to Cézanne", 1940; Los Angeles County
Fair Association, 1950; Pasadena Art Institute, 1950

SLOAN, JOHN (American Contemporary)*   *Plate 123*

OLD CLOWN MAKING UP
canvas 32×26, *painted* 1909, *signed* l.r.: John Sloan
References: Guy Pène Du Bois "John Sloan" (1931), illus.; Martha
Candler Cheney "Modern Art in America" (1939), p. 107; John Sloan
"The Gist of Art" (1939), illus.; Shoolman and Slatkin "The Enjoyment
of Art in America" (1942), p. 686, pl. 663
Exhibited: Baltimore Museum of Art, 1924; Museum of Modern Art,

1929; American Federation of Arts Traveling Exh., 1933; Telfair Academy, Savannah, 1937; Philadelphia Museum of Art "Artists of the Philadelphia Press", 1945, no. 56, illus. in cat.; University of Michigan, 1950

SIX O'CLOCK
canvas 26×32, *painted c.* 1912, *signed* u.l.: John Sloan
References: John Sloan "The Gist of Art" (1939), illus.
Exhibited: American Federation of Arts Traveling Exh., 1931; College Art Association Traveling Exh., 1935–36; Whitney Museum of American Art "New York Realists", 1937, no. 72; Addison Gallery of American Art, Phillips Academy, Andover, 1938; Metropolitan Museum of Art "Life in America", 1939, no. 280, illus. p. 212 in cat.; American Federation of Arts Traveling Exh. of "The Eight", 1940–41; Dallas Museum of Fine Arts "200 Years of American Painting", 1946, no. 20, illus. in cat.; American Federation of Arts Traveling Exh. "The Paintings of John Sloan", 1948–49; Denver Art Museum "Life in America", 1951

THE WAKE OF THE FERRY   *Plate 122*
canvas 26×32, *signed* l.l.: John Sloan 1907
References: A. E. Gallatin "John Sloan" (1925), illus.; F. J. Mather, C. R. Morey, W. J. Henderson "The American Spirit in Art" (1927), illus.; Guy Pène Du Bois "John Sloan" (1931), illus.; John Sloan "The Gist of Art" (1939), illus.; Martha Candler Cheney "Modern Art in America" (1939), p. 107, pl. 65; Peyton Boswell "Modern American Painting" (1939), illus. in color; Oliver W. Larkin "Art and Life in America" (1949), p. 333, illus. p. 333
Exhibited: Venice, Exh. of American Painting, 1924; Museum of Modern Art "Paintings by 19 Living Americans", December 1929–January 1930, no. 83, illus. p. 72 of cat.; Museum of Modern Art, 1936; Cleveland Museum of Art "American Painting from 1860 until Today", 1937; Metropolitan Museum of Art "Life in America", 1939, no. 278, illus. p. 210; Smith College Museum of Art, 1940; Brooklyn Museum "The Eight", 1943, no. 18; Museum of Modern Art Traveling Exh. of "The Eight", 1944; Philadelphia Museum of Art "Artists of the Philadelphia Press", 1945, no. 52; Tate Gallery, London, Exh. of American Paintings, 1946; Brooklyn Museum "The Coast and the Sea", 1949, no. 109; Art Gallery of Toronto, 1950

CONNOISSEURS OF PRINTS
etching $4\frac{1}{2}\times6\frac{3}{4}$, *signed* in pencil l.r.: John Sloan

FIFTH AVENUE CRITICS
etching $4\frac{5}{8}\times6\frac{3}{4}$, *signed* in pencil l.r.: John Sloan

THE HELL HOLE
etching and aquatint $7\frac{7}{8}\times9\frac{3}{4}$, *signed* in pencil l.r.: John Sloan, and on plate l.r.c.: John Sloan 17

HOTEL ENTRANCE
etching $5\times6\frac{7}{8}$, *signed* in pencil l.r.: John Sloan, and on plate l.l.: John Sloan, 1928

McSORLEY'S BACK ROOM
etching 5×7, *signed* in pencil l.r.: John Sloan, and on plate l.l.: John Sloan 16

NIGHT WINDOWS
etching $5\frac{1}{8}\times6\frac{3}{4}$, *signed* in pencil l.r.: John Sloan, and on plate l.l.: John Sloan 1916

THE PICTURE BUYER
etching $5\frac{1}{8}\times6\frac{7}{8}$, *signed* in pencil l.r.: John Sloan

TURNING OUT THE LIGHT
etching $4\frac{7}{8}\times6\frac{7}{8}$, *signed* in pencil l.r.: John Sloan

WOMAN COMBING HER HAIR
etching $3\frac{3}{4}\times2\frac{3}{4}$, *signed* in pencil l.r.: John Sloan

SOROLLA Y BASTIDA, JOAQUIN (Spanish 1863–1923)

ORANGE GROVE
canvas 20×17, *painted* 1902, *unsigned*

SOUTINE, CHAIM (Lithuanian, School of Paris, 1894–1943)

THE PHEASANT   *Plate 175*
canvas $11\frac{3}{4} \times 29\frac{1}{2}$, *signed* l.l.: Soutine
Collections: Henri Matisse

PROFILE (Femme de Profil)   *Plate 172a*
canvas $18\frac{1}{2} \times 11$, *painted* 1937, *signed* l.r.: C. Soutine
References: Monroe Wheeler "Soutine" (1950), p. 100, illus. p. 99
Exhibited: Museum of Modern Art "Soutine", 1950; Cleveland Museum
of Art "Soutine and Modigliani", 1951

THE RETURN FROM SCHOOL (Retour de l' École après L'Orage)   *Plate 174a*
canvas 17×18 (sight dimensions) on stretchers $17 \times 19\frac{1}{2}$,
signed l.r.: C. Soutine
References: Monroe Wheeler "Soutine" (1950), p. 109, illus. p. 106
Exhibited: Museum of Modern Art "Soutine", 1950; Cleveland Museum
of Art "Soutine and Modigliani", 1951

GORGE DU LOUP
canvas $24\frac{3}{4} \times 33\frac{1}{2}$, *signed* l.r.: Soutine

WINDY DAY, AUXERRE   *Plate 174b*
canvas $19\frac{1}{4} \times 25\frac{5}{8}$, *painted* 1939, *unsigned*
References: Monroe Wheeler "Soutine" (1950), p. 109, illus. p. 104
Exhibited: Museum of Modern Art "Soutine", 1950; Cleveland Museum
of Art, "Soutine and Modigliani", 1951

SPEICHER, EUGENE EDWARD (American Contemporary)

GIRL'S HEAD
canvas $22 \times 19\frac{1}{4}$, *painted c.* 1926, *signed* l.c.: Eugene Speicher

SPENCER, NILES (American Contemporary)

DORMER WINDOW
canvas 30×24, *signed* l.r.: Niles Spencer
Exhibited: Cleveland Museum of Art, 1930

GREY BUILDINGS
canvas 20×24, *signed* l.l.: Niles Spencer

SPENCER, ROBERT (American 1879–1931)*

THE AUCTIONEER
canvas 30×36, *signed* l.l.: Robert Spencer
Exhibited: Pennsylvania Academy of the Fine Arts, 1918; Exh. of American Paintings, Venice, 1924

THE EVANGELIST
canvas 25×30, *signed* l.r.: Robert Spencer
References: Shoolman and Slatkin "The Enjoyment of Art in America" (1942), pl. 675
Exhibited: Baltimore Museum of Art, 1924

A MOB AT BAY
canvas 30×36, *signed* l.l.: Robert Spencer
Exhibited: Corcoran Gallery of Art, Biennial Exh., 1929

MOUNTEBANKS AND THIEVES
canvas 30×36, *signed* l.r.: Robert Spencer
Exhibited: National Academy of Design, 1925; Carnegie Institute, Pittsburgh, 1925; American Exh., Budapest, 1930; Biennale Exh., Venice, 1930; Carnegie Institute, Pittsburgh, 1935

ON THE BANK
canvas 14×12, *signed* l.r.: Robt. Spencer

SHIP CHANDLERS' ROW   *Plate 196*
canvas 30×36, *signed* l.r.: Robert Spencer
Exhibited: Corcoran Gallery of Art, Biennial Exh., 1926

WOMAN IRONING
canvas 14×12, *signed* l.l.: Robt. Spencer

SPRINCHORN, CARL (American Contemporary)

IN SPAIN
gouache $11\frac{5}{8}×9\frac{1}{8}$, *painted c.* 1916, *signed* l.r.: C. S.

SNOW-WINGED HORSES
canvas 36 × 38, *painted* 1921, *signed* l.l.: Carl Sprinchorn
Exhibited: Arts Club of Chicago, 1922; Worcester Art Museum, 1922

STERNE, MAURICE (American Contemporary)*

AFTER RAIN   Plate 194a
canvas 24 × 30, *signed* l.r.: Sterne '47

AFTERNOON AT ANTICOLI
canvas 45 × 32, *signed* l.r.: Sterne 1924
Exhibited: Museum of Modern Art "Maurice Sterne", 1933, no. 64, illus.
in cat.; Art Institute of Chicago, Century of Progress Exh., 1933, no.
649, illus. in cat.; Syracuse Museum of Fine Arts, 1939; Art Institute
of Chicago "Half a Century of American Art", 1939

BENARES   Plate 168
canvas 40 × 30, *signed* l.r.: Sterne, Benares, 1912
Exhibited: Whitney Museum of American Art "Pioneers of Modern Art
in America", 1946, and American Federation of Arts Traveling Exh.
of this show

GIRL WITH PINK KERCHIEF
canvas 16¾ × 13¾, *unsigned*

MOTHER AND CHILD   Plate 169
canvas 25½ × 19¾, *signed* l.l.: Sterne

THE REAPERS
canvas 27¾ × 49, *painted* 1925, *signed* l.r.: Sterne
References: Sheldon Cheney "A Primer of Modern Art" (1932), illus.
Exhibited: Museum of Modern Art "Maurice Sterne", 1933, no. 69; Art
Institute of Chicago, Century of Progress Exh., 1934, no. 698; Syracuse
Museum of Fine Arts, 1939

STILL LIFE
canvas 20 × 24¾, *painted* 1925, *signed* l.r.: Maurice Sterne
Exhibited: Baltimore Museum of Art, 1927; Museum of Modern Art
"Maurice Sterne", 1933, no. 70

TEMPLE FEAST, BALI
oil on paper 21¼ × 19¼, *unsigned*

STIEGLITZ, ALFRED (American 1864–1946)

EQUIVALENTS
(Gift of Georgia O'Keeffe)
Set of 19 photographs, each approximately $3\frac{1}{2} \times 4\frac{1}{2}$

TACK, AUGUSTUS VINCENT (American 1870–1949)*

ASPIRATION   Plate 127
mural on canvas $76\frac{1}{2} \times 135\frac{1}{2}$, *painted c. 1931, unsigned*
Exhibited: Wildenstein, New York, 1934

CHRISTMAS NIGHT
canvas mounted on composition panel 69×43, *signed* l.r.: Tack
Exhibited: Abbot Academy, Andover, 1941

THE CROWD
canvas mounted on composition panel 15×36, *signed* l.r.: Tack
Exhibited: Abbot Academy, Andover, 1941

ECSTASY
lunette on canvas mounted on composition panel $47\frac{3}{4} \times 64$, *signed* l.r.:
Tack
Exhibited: Wildenstein, New York, 1934

THE ENTOMBMENT
canvas mounted on wood 29×40, *painted 1924, signed* l.l.c.: Tack
Exhibited: American Exh., Budapest, 1930; Biennale Exh., Venice, 1930;
Washington County Museum of Fine Arts, Hagerstown, 1938; Howard
University Art Gallery, 1940; Abbot Academy, Andover, 1941;
Institute of Contemporary Art, Boston, "Modern Religious Art", 1944,
no. 104

GETHSEMANE
canvas mounted on wood panel $15\frac{3}{4} \times 37\frac{1}{4}$, *signed* l.r.: Tack
Exhibited: Institute of Contemporary Art, Boston, "Modern Religious
Art", 1944

LARGO
canvas mounted on composition panel 44×36, *signed* l.r.: Tack
Exhibited: Museum of Modern Art "Living Americans", 1930; Wildenstein, New York, 1934

LIBERATION
lunette on canvas mounted on composition panel 47¾×64, *signed* l.r.c.: Tack
Exhibited: Wildenstein, New York, 1934

NIGHT, AMARGOSA DESERT
canvas mounted on composition panel 84×48, *signed* l.l.: Augustus Vincent Tack
Exhibited: Corcoran Gallery of Art, Biennial Exh., 1937

NIGHT CLOUDS AND STAR DUST
canvas mounted on composition panel 75×42, *signed* l.r.: Augustus Vincent Tack

PASSACAGLIA   Plate 124
tondo on canvas mounted on composition panel 43×49, *signed* l.r.: Tack
Exhibited: Baltimore Museum of Art, 1927; John Herron Art Institute, Indianapolis, 1931; Washington County Museum of Fine Arts, Hagers-town, 1938; Abbot Academy, Andover, 1941

PORTRAIT OF THE HON. ELIHU ROOT
canvas 48×36, *signed* l.r. side: Tack
Exhibited: Exh. of American Painting, Venice, 1924; Yale University Art Gallery, 1931; Washington County Museum of Fine Arts, Hagers-town, 1938; Abbot Academy, Andover, 1941; National Gallery of Art, Washington, 1950

PORTRAIT OF ELWOOD HENDRICK
wood panel 40×29, *signed* l.l.: Tack
Exhibited: Washington County Museum of Fine Arts, Hagerstown, 1938

SPRING NIGHT
canvas mounted on composition panel 68¾×43½, *signed* l.r.; Tack
Exhibited: Abbot Academy, Andover, 1941

STORM   Plate 126
canvas mounted on composition panel 37×48, *signed* l.r.: Tack
Exhibited: Baltimore Museum of Art, 1934; Art Institute of Chicago, Century of Progress Exh., 1934, no. 702; George Walter Vincent Smith Art Museum, Springfield, 1936; Washington County Museum of Fine Arts, Hagerstown, 1938; Abbot Academy, Andover, 1941

TIME AND TIMELESSNESS
canvas 35 × 83, *signed* l.l. vertically: Augustus Vincent Tack
Exhibited: Tate Gallery, London, Exhibition of American Painting, 1946

THE VOICE OF MANY WATERS   Plate 125
canvas mounted on composition panel 76½ × 48, *painted c.* 1924,
signed l.l.: Tack
Exhibited: Carnegie Institute, Pittsburgh, International Exh., 1928; John
Herron Art Institute, Indianapolis, 1931; Wildenstein, New York, 1934

And nine decorative panels

TOBEY, MARK

MARRIAGE   Plate 238a
tempera on masonite panel 6 × 21, *signed* l.l.: Tobey '45

TRAVI, ANTONIO (Italian 1608–1665)

OLD TESTAMENT LANDSCAPE   Plate 2
canvas 29½ × 40, *unsigned*
Collections: Private collection, England

TUCKER, ALLEN (American 1866–1939)

BUNKER HILL
canvas 30 × 36, *signed* l.r.: Allen Tucker

THE ORANGE BOOK
canvas 24 × 20, *signed* l.l.c.: Allen Tucker

RED BARNS
canvas 25 × 30½, *signed* l.r.: Allen Tucker
Exhibited: Copenhagen, Stockholm, Munich, Exh. of American Painting, 1930; Whitney Museum of American Art, Allen Tucker Memorial
Exh., 1940

THE RISE
canvas 30½ × 36, *signed* l.r.: Allen Tucker

THE SQUALL
canvas 29½×50½, *signed* l.r.: Allen Tucker
Exhibited: Whitney Museum of American Art, Allen Tucker Memorial
Exh., 1940, illus. in cat.

TREE AND BARN
watercolor 14½×20¾, *signed* l.l.: Allen Tucker

TURNER, HELEN (American Contemporary)

A DEBUTANTE
canvas 24×16, *signed* u.l.: Helen M. Turner 1916

ON A RAINY DAY
canvas 16×12, *signed* l.r.: Helen M. Turner

TURNER, JOSEPH MALLORD WILLIAM (English 1775–1851)

COAST SCENE WITH SAILS   Plate 10a
wood panel 9⅞×11¹⁵⁄₁₆, *unsigned*
Collections: J. N. Laurvik

TWACHTMAN, JOHN HENRY (American 1853–1902)

EMERALD POOL   Plate 77
canvas 25×25, *signed* l.r.: J. H. Twachtman
Exhibited: Baltimore Museum of Art, 1934; Metropolitan Museum of
Art, 1934

MY AUTUMN STUDIO
canvas 30×30, *unsigned*

SPRING
pastel 14×11, *signed* l.l.: J. H. Twachtman

SUMMER   Plate 76
canvas 30×53, *signed* l.r.: J. H. Twachtman
References: Eliot Candee Clark "John Twachtman" (1924), illus.; F. J.
Mather, C. R. Morey, W. J. Henderson "The American Spirit in Art"

(1927), illus.; Allen Tucker "John H. Twachtman" (1931), illus.; Shoolman and Slatkin "The Enjoyment of Art in America" (1942), p. 684, pl. 652
Exhibited: Virginia Museum of Fine Arts "Main Currents in the Development of American Painting", 1936, no. 81, illus. in cat.; Brooklyn Museum "Leaders of American Impressionism", 1937, no. 69; Carnegie Institute, Pittsburgh "A Survey of American Painting", 1940, no. 163; M. Knoedler, New York "Loan Exh. in Honor of Royal Cortissoz", 1941, no. 32

WINTER
canvas $21\frac{1}{2} \times 26$, *signed* l.r.: J. H. Twachtman
Exhibited: Newark Museum Association, 1931

UTRILLO, MAURICE (French Contemporary)

ABBEY OF SAINT-DENIS   Plate 164
canvas $28\frac{1}{2} \times 19\frac{1}{2}$, *painted* 1910, *signed* l.l.: Maurice Utrillo, V.
Collections: Defrenne, Paris
Exhibited: Amsterdam and The Hague "L'Art Français", 1936; Dudley Peter Allen Memorial Art Museum, Oberlin College, 1940

VERDILHAN, MATHIEU (French Contemporary)

FRUIT AND FLOWERS
canvas $24\frac{1}{2} \times 32$, *signed* l.r.: Verdilhan—Mathieu

VILLON, JACQUES (French Contemporary)

THE GRAIN DOES NOT DIE (Le Grain ne Meurt)   Plate 145a
canvas $25\frac{1}{4} \times 55\frac{1}{8}$, *painted* 1947, *signed* l.l.: Jacques Villon
Exhibited: Institute of Contemporary Art, Boston; The Phillips Gallery, Washington; Delaware Art Center, Wilmington, Villon-Feininger Exh., 1949–50, no. 24, illus. in cat.; Biennale Exh., Venice, 1950

THE LITTLE MACHINE SHOP (Le Petit Atelier de Mécanique)   Plate 145b
canvas $31\frac{7}{8} \times 45\frac{3}{8}$, *painted* 1946, *signed* l.r.: Jacques Villon

THE MACHINE SHOP (L'Atelier de Mécanique)
canvas 29 × 36¼, *signed* l.l.: Jacques Villon 13
Collections: Walter Pach

VOLLON, ANTOINE (French 1833–1900)

VIOLETS
canvas 9½ × 13, *signed* l.l.: A. Vollon

VUILLARD, JEAN ÉDOUARD (French 1867–1940)

THE NEWSPAPER   Plate 98
composition panel 13½ × 21½, *signed* u.r.: Vuillard
Exhibited: Syracuse Museum of Fine Arts, 1930; Rochester Memorial Art
Gallery, 1930; Philadelphia Museum of Art, 1935; Art Institute of
Chicago, Bonnard–Vuillard Exh., 1938–39, no. 41; Akron Art Institute,
1947

*NURSE WITH A CHILD IN SAILOR SUIT (Nounou avec Enfant
en Sailor)*
composition panel 9 × 9½, *signed* l.r.: E. Vuillard 95
Exhibited: Art Institute of Chicago, Bonnard–Vuillard Exh., 1939, no. 27

WAITING (La Visite)   Plate 101
composition board mounted on canvas 23½ × 20, *painted* 1900,
signed u.r.: E. Vuillard
Collections: Gaston Bernheim de Villers
References: Claude Roger–Marx "Vuillard, his life and work" (1946),
p. 64

WOMAN SWEEPING (Femme Balayant dans un Intérieur)   Plate 99
composition panel 18 × 19, *painted* c. 1892, *signed* l.r.: E. Vuillard
Collections: Josse Bernheim
References: Daniel Catton Rich "Bonnard and Vuillard" (foreword to
cat. of Bonnard–Vuillard Exh., Art Institute of Chicago, 1938–39)
Exhibited: Berlin, 1903; Art Institute of Chicago, Bonnard–Vuillard
Exh., December 1938–January 1939, no. 25, illus. in cat.

And one color lithograph

VYTLACIL, VACLAV (American Contemporary)

WOOD INTERIOR   *Plate 233*
composition panel 32 × 40, *signed* l.r.: Vaclav Vytlacil 1949

WALKOWITZ, ABRAHAM (American Contemporary)

IN THE PARK
watercolor 21¾ × 29¾, *signed* l.r.: A. Walkowitz

WALTHER, CHARLES H. (American 1879–1938)

ABSTRACT LANDSCAPE
composition panel 20 × 10, *signed* l.r.c.: C. H. Walther

WATKINS, C. LAW (American 1886–1945)

MOUNTAIN LANDSCAPE
· canvas board panel 12 × 16, *unsigned*

WATKINS, FRANKLIN C. (American Contemporary)

THE ANGEL WILL TURN A PAGE IN THE BOOK   *Plate 216*
canvas 33 × 28, *painted* 1944, *signed* l.r.: Watkins
Exhibited: Carnegie Institute, Pittsburgh, 1944; Art Gallery of Toronto,
1945; Armory, New York, 1945; Art Institute of Chicago, 1945; Rhode
Island School of Design, 1946; Art Gallery of Toronto, 1949; Museum
of Modern Art "Franklin C. Watkins", 1950, no. 35, illus. in cat.

AUTUMN RECOLLECTIONS   *Plate 217*
canvas 28 × 32, *signed* l.r.: Watkins 40
Exhibited: Art Alliance, Philadelphia, 1945; Philadelphia Museum of
Art, Carles-Watkins Exh., 1946, no. 53; Santa Barbara Museum of
Art, 1949; Portland Art Museum, 1949; Museum of Modern Art
"Franklin C. Watkins", 1950, no. 26

PORTRAIT OF BORIS BLAI
canvas 31×29, *painted c.* 1935, *signed* u.r.: F. W.
Exhibited: Carnegie Institute, Pittsburgh, International Exh., 1939, no. 59;
Detroit Institute of Arts, 1942; Philadelphia Museum of Art, Carles⁄
Watkins Exh., 1946, no. 45; Wilmington Society of the Fine Arts, 1947

WATTEAU, JEAN ANTOINE (French 1684–1721)

MUSICIANS
sanguine drawing 4⅝×7½, *unsigned*
Collections: David Weill, Paris

WEBER, MAX (American Contemporary)*

AFTER AN ICE STORM   Plate 194b
canvas 30×36, *painted c.* 1943, *signed* l.r.: Max Weber

COLONIAL BOWL
canvas 19×22, *painted c.* 1941, *signed* l.r.: Max Weber

CONVERSATION
gouache 4½×5, *signed* u.r.: Max Weber
Exhibited: Art Institute of Chicago, 1942

DRAPED HEAD   Plate 172b
canvas 21×13, *painted* 1924, *signed* l.r.: Max Weber
Exhibited: Baltimore Museum of Art, 1927; Museum of Modern Art
"Max Weber", 1930, no. 99; Walker Art Center, Minneapolis, 1949;
Whitney Museum of American Art, Weber Retrospective Exh., 1949

HIGH NOON
canvas 20×24, *painted c.* 1925, *signed* l.r.: Max Weber

RABBI
canvas 20×16, *signed* l.l.: Max Weber

STUDENTS OF THE TORAH
canvas 25×32, *signed* l.r.: Max Weber
Exhibited: Art Gallery of Toronto, 1945

WEINRICH, AGNES (American 1880–1946)

STILL LIFE
canvas 18×24, *signed* l.r.: A. Weinrich

WEIR, JULIAN ALDEN (American 1852–1919)*

AFTERNOON BY THE POND
canvas 25×30, *signed* l.l.: J. Alden Weir

THE FISHING PARTY
canvas 28×23, *painted* 1910–19, *unsigned*
Exhibited: Metropolitan Museum of Art, Weir Memorial Exh., 1924;
Whitney Museum of American Art "A Century of American Land‚
scape Painting", 1938, no. 66; Carnegie Institute, Pittsburgh "A Century
of American Landscape Painting", 1939, no. 11

KNITTING FOR SOLDIERS
canvas 30×24½, *painted* 1910–19, *signed* u.r.: J. Alden Weir
Exhibited: Metropolitan Museum of Art, Weir Memorial Exh., 1924

A LANE IN SPRING
wood panel 10¼×15¾, *signed* l.l.: J. Alden Weir

PAN AND THE WOLF   Plate 78
canvas 34×24, *painted c.* 1917, *signed* l.l.: J. Alden Weir
Exhibited: Carnegie Institute, Pittsburgh, 1910; Metropolitan Museum
of Art, Weir Memorial Exh., 1924; Brooklyn Museum "Leaders of
American Impressionism", 1937, no. 79

ROSES
canvas 35×25, *painted* 1880–89, *signed* u.r.: J. Alden Weir
Exhibited: Metropolitan Museum of Art, Weir Memorial Exh., 1924,
illus. in cat.; Baltimore Museum of Art, 1945

VISITING NEIGHBORS   Plate 79
canvas 24½×34, *painted* 1900–09, *signed* l.r.: J. Alden Weir
Exhibited: Metropolitan Museum of Art, Weir Memorial Exh., 1924

WOODLAND ROCKS
canvas 28×36, *painted* 1910–19, *signed* l.r.: J. Alden Weir
Exhibited: Metropolitan Museum of Art, Weir Memorial Exh., 1924

References to many of the above paintings by Weir are in "Julian Alden Weir, An Appreciation" (The Phillips Publications Number One, 1922)

WESTON, HAROLD (American Contemporary)*

THE ARENA   Plate 225b
canvas 18×24, *signed* l.l.: W. 30

CONVALESCING
gouache 13$\frac{3}{8}$×9$\frac{1}{2}$, *signed* l.r.: Weston 38
Exhibited: Art Institute of Chicago, 1940

DOS PASSOS READING
canvas 22×16, *signed* u.r. side: Weston

IN THE STUDIO
gouache 25$\frac{3}{8}$×19$\frac{3}{4}$, *signed* l.l.: Weston

LONELINESS   Plate 225a
canvas 13×22, *painted c.* 1930, *signed* l.l.: Weston
Exhibited: Tate Gallery, London, Exh. of American Paintings, 1946

MELONS
canvas 18×15, *signed* l.r.: W.

THE NEW STOVE
canvas 21$\frac{3}{4}$×15, *signed* l.r. side: W.

PASSAGEWAY
canvas 20×18, *signed* l.l.: Weston

PORTRAIT OF N. E. MONTROSS
canvas 24×20, *signed* u.l.: Weston

PURRING
canvas 13×18, *signed* l.l.: Weston

PUSSY WILLOWS
canvas 22×13, *signed* l.l.: Weston

SELF PORTRAIT
canvas 18×14, *signed* l.r.: Weston

SNOW BLOWING IN THE PASS
gouache 11¼×19½, *signed* l.r.: Weston 40

SNOW SHOES
canvas 38×26, *signed* l.l.: Weston

SNOW SQUALLS
gouache 9½×13½, *signed* l.l.: Weston 35

SPRING IN THE PYRENEES
canvas 14⅞×18, *painted* 1935, *signed* l.l.: Weston
Exhibited: San Francisco Museum of Art, 1939; Pennsylvania Academy
of Fine Arts, 1939

WHISTLER, JAMES ABBOTT McNEILL (American 1834–1903)

MISS LILLIAN WOAKES   *Plate 43*
canvas 21×14, *painted* 1890–91, *signed* twice with the butterfly
(in bow of dress and above shoulder, l.c.)
Collections: Dr. E. G. Woakes, London
References: E. R. and J. Pennell "Whistler" (1911), p. 356; Elizabeth
Luther Cary "Whistler" (1913), no. 380, p. 213; T. Duret "Whistler"
(Paris, 1914), illus. opp. p. 146; N. Pousette-Dart "James McNeill
Whistler" (1924), illus.; James W. Lane "Whistler" (1942), illus.
Exhibited: New Gallery, London, Whistler Memorial Exh., 1905, no. 20;
Albright Art Gallery, Buffalo, 1912; M. Knoedler, New York, Whistler
Exh., 1914, no. 3, illus. in cat.; Art Institute of Chicago, Century of
Progress Exh., 1934, no. 428

WOOD, CHRISTOPHER (English 1901–1930)

HOUSE BY THE SEA
watercolor 10¾×14¾, *painted* 1925, *unsigned*

TIGER AND ARC DE TRIOMPHE · *Plate 207b*
canvas 18¼×21¾, *painted* 1930, *unsigned*
Collections: Clara D. Wood; Rex Nan Kivell, Esq.
References: Eric Newton "Christopher Wood" (1938), no. 380, illus. p. 64

YEATS, JACK B. (Irish Contemporary)

AFTER-DINNER COFFEE IN A CITY · *Plate 235*
canvas 24×36, *signed* l.l.: Jack B. Yeats

YOUNG, MAHONRI (American Contemporary)

THE BLACKSMITH
bronze 12 in. high, *signed* r. corner of base: M. M. Young

ON THE MAJESTIC
watercolor 10½×9¾, *signed* l.l.c.: Mahonri Young, Majestic, May 1923

STREET IN PARIS
watercolor with ink 9×5⅝, *signed* l.r.: Mahonri Young, Paris

And two drawings and six etchings

ZORACH, WILLIAM (American Contemporary)

SAILING BY MOONLIGHT · *Plate 249*
watercolor 21½×14¾, *signed* l.r.: Zorach 1922

THE YELLOW MAST
watercolor 15½×11, *signed* l.r.: Zorach 1922

ZULOAGA Y ZABALESA, IGNACIO (Spanish 1870–1945)

A GIRL OF MONTMARTRE
canvas 32×24, *signed* l.r.: I. Zuloaga

PART II: THE COLLECTION CONTINUED

This section, consisting mostly of younger contemporary artists, includes other Exhibition Units, and paintings purchased not only by the Collection but by Mr. and Mrs. Phillips.

ABRAMOWITZ, BENJAMIN

LABYRINTH
canvas 34×24, *signed* l.r.c.: Abramowitz 49

ACHESON, ALICE

CONVENT GARDEN
canvas board panel 16×20, *painted c.* 1944, *signed* l.r.: Alice Acheson

ADES, ROBERT

BLITZKRIEG
canvas 34×18, *signed*: R. Ades 40

ARLT, PAUL

BAR PACO
watercolor 15×22½, *signed* l.r.: Paul T. Arlt '39

BUS TO AMECAMECA
canvas 18×38, *signed* l.l.: Paul Arlt

ARNER, ROBERT

LILACS
canvas 27×22, *painted c.* 1941, *signed* on back: Arner

ATKYNS, LEE

FESTIVAL
canvas board $10\frac{1}{2}\times18$, painted 1946, *signed* l.r.c.: Lee Atkyns

AUSTIN, DARREL

DARK RIVER
canvas 20×24, *signed* l.r.: Darrel Austin

BAKER, SARAH

THE CRISTIANIS REHEARSING
canvas 20×24, *unsigned*

THE PITCHER
canvas 16×23, *unsigned*

BAND, MAX (Lithuanian-American Contemporary)

PARIS ROOFS
canvas $15\times21\frac{3}{4}$, *signed* l.r.: Max Band

BARRETT, TOM

DOWNTOWN POUGHKEEPSIE
canvas 24×36, *signed* l.r.: Tom Barrett '40

BARTHÉ, RICHMOND

JOHN THE BAPTIST
plaster, toned bronze, $13\frac{1}{2}$ in. high, *signed* on back: Barthé

BATTAGLIA, EDITH

BARN
oil on paper $7\frac{1}{8}\times16$, *unsigned*

BENOIT, RIGAUD (Haitian Contemporary)

WATERFALL
oil on cardboard 30×24, *signed* u.r.: R. Benoit

BEN-ZION

ABSTRACT ROOSTER
wood panel 11½×17¾, *signed* l.r.: Ben-Zion

BERNSTEIN, THERESA

GIRLHOOD
canvas 29×35, *signed* u.r.: T. Bernstein 21

BERTOIA, HARRY

Untitled monoprint 9×6⅝, *unsigned*

BIALA, JANICE

SPRING, RUE DE SEINE
composition panel 21¾×26, *signed* l.r.: Biala 36

BINFORD, JULIAN

WORK
canvas 11½×29½, *unsigned*

BISHOP, ISABEL

LUNCH COUNTER
masonite panel 23×14, *painted c.* 1940, *unsigned*

BOHANAN, WALTER

SAIL AND PIER
canvas 13×18, *signed* l.r.: Bohanan '32

BOLOTOWSKY, ILYA

ABSTRACTION
canvas 18×24, *signed* l.r.: Ilya Bolotowsky

BONBRIGHT, SYBIL

GREEN APPLES
canvas 16×20, *painted c.* 1944, *unsigned*

BOOKATZ, SAMUEL

PRAYER
oil on paper 19¾×26, *signed* u.l.: Bookatz

BOSSHARD, R. H. (Swiss Contemporary)

BLUE GRAPES AND PEARS
plywood panel 12×15½, *signed* l.l.: R. H. Bosshard '37

BOTKIN, HENRY

MOUNTAIN ROAD
canvas 24×34, *painted c.* 1939, *signed* l.l.: Botkin

BUK (ULREICH)

THE GATHERING OF THE CHIEFS
composition panel 24×19¾, *signed* l.r.: Buk

BURG, COPELAND

FRUITS AND FLOWERS
masonite panel 16×20, *signed* u.l.: Copeland

BURGESS, MARGUERITE

NURSEMAIDS IN THE PARK
canvas 12×18, *painted* 1941, *signed* l.r.: M. Burgess

CALDER, ALEXANDER

RED FLOCK
metal and wire mobile sculpture 33½ in. high, *executed c.* 1949–50

CALFEE, WILLIAM

DIGRESSION
canvas 20×24, *signed* l.r.: Calfee 44

EARTHWARD IN CITY FALL
canvas 12×16, *painted* 1943, *unsigned*

CHARLOT, JEAN (French-American Contemporary)

CUP AND DICE
canvas 14×11, *signed* l.c.: Jean Charlot 25

LEOPARD HUNTER
canvas 11×14, *signed* l.l.: Charlot

MEXICAN NIGHT
canvas 11×14, *unsigned*

CIKOVSKY, NICOLAI

WINTER LANDSCAPE
canvas 20×30, *signed* l.r.: N. Cikovsky 36

CLARKE, LIZ

TREASURE ISLAND
paper collage and oil on canvas 15×20, *executed* 1942, *unsigned*

COALE, DONALD

NIGHT SCENE
masonite panel 18×22, *painted* 1940, *unsigned*

CONOVER, ALIDA

MORNING IN THE PARK
canvas 16×24, *signed* l.r.: Alida Conover '38

CRAWFORD, RALSTON

BOAT AND GRAIN ELEVATORS   Plate 253
masonite panel 20×16, *signed* l.l.: Crawford

CROSS, BERNICE*

ANCESTRESS
canvas 38×32, *painted* 1950, *unsigned*

HALLELUJAH
canvas 34×28, *painted* 1941, *unsigned*

IRIS
canvas 15×10, *painted* 1938, *unsigned*

THE KEY
canvas with collage 33×20, *painted* 1946, *unsigned*

KEY RACK
canvas 18×25, *painted* 1949, *unsigned*

LAND OF COTTON
canvas 21×16, *painted* 1938, *unsigned*

LI PO
oil on paper mounted on masonite 14×20, *painted* 1940, *unsigned*

THE MANSION
cloth collage 16×12, *executed* 1944, *unsigned*

PANSIES AND PITCHER
canvas 14×24, *painted* 1948, *unsigned*

PINK LEMONADE
canvas 12×14, *painted* 1941, *unsigned*

SEED CATALOGUE
canvas with collage 10×12, *painted* 1942, *unsigned*

STONE ANGEL   *Plate 251*
canvas 24×14, *painted* 1950, *unsigned*

STOVE
oil on velvet 18×10, *painted* 1940, *unsigned*

STRAWBERRY BASKET   *Plate 250a*
collage on canvas 10×12, *executed c.* 1945, *unsigned*

'STUTE FISH
canvas 14×18, *painted* 1948, *unsigned*

SUNKEN TREASURE   *Plate 250b*
canvas with collage 18×20, *painted* 1944, *unsigned*

WINTER LIGHT
canvas 18×34, *painted* 1950, *unsigned*

CZÓBEL, BÉLA (Hungarian Contemporary, School of Paris)

PITCHER AND FLOWERS
canvas 38½×31, *painted c.* 1936, *signed* l.r.: Czóbel

DAY, JERRY

FISH
canvas 12×20, *unsigned*

DE DIEGO, JULIO

SOUTHERN FRONT CRUMBLES
masonite panel 12×16, *signed* l.r.: de Diego 43

DI GIOIA, FRANK (Italian-American Contemporary)

PROCESSION
gouache $4 \times 5\frac{3}{4}$, *painted c.* 1938, *signed* l.r.: F. di Gioia 37

DONATO, LOUIS

LANDSCAPE
canvas 20×26, *signed* l.l.: L. Donato 38

DOUGLAS, LAURA

IMPRESSIONS OF CYPRESS GARDENS
gouache and paper collage $8\frac{1}{2} \times 11$, *signed* l.r.: Laura Glenn Douglas

SYMPHONY No. 2, CHARLESTON
gouache and ink $17\frac{3}{4} \times 23\frac{1}{2}$, *signed* l.l.: Laura Glenn Douglas '34

DOVE, WILLIAM

WHARF CLEAT
oil on cardboard 12×9, *unsigned*

DOWS, OLIN

AFTER RAIN
gouache $7 \times 19\frac{1}{2}$, *painted* 1938, *unsigned*

REFRESHMENT TENT
wood panel 11×21, *signed* l.r.: Olin Dows '34

DRIGGS, ELSIE

AT THE RACES
gouache $15\frac{3}{4} \times 24$, *signed* l.r.: Driggs

DUNN, CHARLES

'CELLIST
composition panel 16 × 12, *painted* 1936, *unsigned*

DWIGHT, MABEL

THREE LITHOGRAPHS
(Dwight Clark Bequest)

DYER, BRIGGS

ANN ARBOR LANDSCAPE
canvas 33 × 40, *signed* l.r.: Dyer 41

ECKEL, JULIA

THE LUTE PLAYER
canvas 12 × 10, *painted* 1939, *signed* on back: Eckel

EDZARD, DIETZ (German Contemporary)

FRUIT AND PLATE
canvas mounted on wood panel $7\frac{5}{8}$ × 10, *signed* l.l.: d. Edzard

EMMERICH, JANET

STILL LIFE
oil on paper $17\frac{1}{2}$ × 24, *painted* 1936, *unsigned*

ETNIER, STEPHEN

PIER END
canvas 20 × 24, *signed* l.l.: Stephen Etnier '40

STREET CORNER, CHARLESTON
canvas 30 × 28, *painted c.* 1935, *signed* l.l.: Stephen Etnier

EVANS, LUCILE

FRUITION
wax medium on paper 22×26, *painted* 1946–48, *signed* l.r.: Lucile Evans

FISHER, MARGARET

GIRL IN YELLOW SWEATER
canvas 20×16, *signed* l.r.c.: M. Fisher

LANDSCAPE, NEW MEXICO
watercolor 8¼×11½, *signed* l.l.: M. Fisher

FOLINSBEE, JOHN

ALONG THE CANAL
canvas 16×20, *signed* l.r.: John F. Folinbsee

GÁG, WANDA (American 1893–1946)

LAMPLIGHT
lithograph 10¾×8½, *signed* on paper, l.r.: Wanda Gág 29
(Dwight Clark Bequest)

GATES, MARGARET

GOLDFISH
canvas-board 18×21, *painted* 1948, *signed* l.l.: Margaret Gates

LANDSCAPE, COLORADO
canvas 16×24, *painted* 1938, *unsigned*

SURBURBAN MORNING
casein tempera on paper 15¾×22, *painted* 1944, *unsigned*

GATES, ROBERT FRANKLIN*

AUTUMN GOLD
canvas 26×36, *signed* l.l.: R. Gates 49

BEACH THINGS
canvas 22×26, *signed* l.l.: R. Gates 47

THE MILL POND, CHATHAM
watercolor 15¼×21, *signed* l.r.: Robert Franklin Gates, Chatham, Cape Cod, 1938

NIGHT SONG
composition panel 21¾×30, *signed* l.l.: R. Gates '50

POTOMAC RIVER ICE BREAKER
watercolor 15×21, *signed* l.r.: Robert Franklin Gates 1936

RISING CLIFFS
watercolor 15×20¾, *signed* l.l.: Robert Franklin Gates, Colorado, 1938

SCOTT CIRCLE
watercolor 21¼×29¼, *signed* l.l.: Robert Franklin Gates

SHERIDAN CIRCLE
watercolor 20½×28½, *painted* 1935, *unsigned*

SUNFLOWER   Plate 254
tempera on watercolor board 30×21⅞, *signed* l.r.: R. Gates '49

THISTLE AND FERN
watercolor 15½×21½, *signed* l.r.: Robert Franklin Gates, West Va., 1937

WATERFRONT, ST. THOMAS
watercolor 15¾×21, *signed* l.r.: Robert Franklin Gates, St. Thomas, V. I., 1936

WINTER EVENING, FOGGY BOTTOM
watercolor 14¾×20¼, *signed* l.r.: Robert Franklin Gates 1936

GERARD, JOSEPH

HIGH TIDE   Plate 239b
canvas 30×36, *painted c.* 1946, *signed* l.l.c.: Gerard

GERNAND, JOHN*

BLOWING LEAVES
canvas 12×16, *painted* 1944, *signed* l.l.: Gernand

Plate 239a

CIRCUS RINGS
canvas 12×19, *painted* 1942, *signed* l.l.: Gernand

CITY
canvas 16×10, *painted* 1945, *signed* l.l.: Gernand

EVENING GARDEN
canvas 12×22, *painted* 1938, *signed* l.r.: Gernand

MEMORY OF NIGHT, ST. THOMAS
canvas 36×28, *painted* 1938, *signed* l.r.: John Gernand

VIGNETTED BOUQUET
canvas 12×16, *painted* 1946, *signed* l.c.: Gernand

THE VOYAGE OF BACCHUS
canvas 20×16, *painted* 1943, *signed* l.l.: Gernand

WINDOW AND FLOWERS
canvas 26×20, *painted* 1947, *signed* l.r.c.: Gernand

GIESE, HAROLD

ANCIENT MEETING
casein tempera on paper $9\frac{3}{8}$×$12\frac{1}{2}$, *signed* l.r.: H. Giese '49

BANANAS
oil on paper, mounted on masonite $9\frac{1}{2}$×$13\frac{7}{8}$, *painted c.* 1946, *unsigned*

Plate 248a

RONDO No. 2
tondo 17 in. in diameter on canvas 18×18, *painted c.* 1944, *unsigned*

GLUSHAKOW, JACOB

CITY PARK
composition panel 10×14, *signed* l.r.: J. Glushakow 39

GOCHNAUER, MARSHALL

APPALACHIAN MOUNTAINS
collage on masonite 14¼×20½, *executed* 1948, *signed* l.r.: Gochnauer

GRAVES, MORRIS*

CHALICE   *Plate 246*
gouache on rice paper 27×29¾, *unsigned*

EAGLE   *Plate 244*
gouache on rice paper 21×36, *unsigned*

IN THE NIGHT
gouache on rice paper 30×26, *unsigned*

SANDERLINGS
gouache on rice paper 25×30, *painted* 1943, *unsigned*

SURF AND BIRD
gouache on rice paper 26¼×29¼, *signed* l.r.: M. Graves

WOUNDED GULL   *Plate 245*
gouache on rice paper 23×28, *signed* l.l.: M. Graves /43

YOUNG PINE FOREST IN BLOOM
tempera on rice paper 30¼×25⅛, *signed* l.r.: M. Graves 47

HALEY, JOHN

SHEEP
canvas 20×40, *signed* l.r.: John Haley

HIRSCH, STEFAN

MILL TOWN
canvas 30×40, *unsigned*

MANHATTAN
canvas 29×34, *signed* l.l.: S.H. 1921

JAMIESON, MITCHELL

DEATH OF A CITY
tempera and ink on paper $21\frac{1}{4} \times 27\frac{1}{2}$, *signed* l.r.: M. Jamieson '46

JONES, LOIS

PLACE DU TERTRE
canvas $18\frac{1}{4} \times 21\frac{3}{4}$, *signed* l.r.: Lois M. Jones, Paris '38

JULES, MERVIN

BURLESQUE
composition panel 8×13, *signed* l.r.: Jules

JUNYER, JŌAN (Spanish-American Contemporary)

PARADE, FROM "CONGAS"
Sgraffito in red clay on cardboard $10\frac{1}{4} \times 12\frac{1}{2}$, *signed* l.l.: Jōan Junyer

KAINEN, JACOB

HOT DOG CART
canvas 24×30, *painted* 1943, *signed* l.r.: Kainen

THE OLD CANAL
canvas 24×30, *painted* c. 1948, *signed* l.r.: Kainen

SLEEP
beaver board panel 12×16, *signed* l.l.: Kainen

KAMROWSKI, GEROME

PEOPLE
canvas $9\frac{3}{4} \times 22\frac{1}{4}$, *signed* l.l.c.: Kamrowski

KIKOÏNE, MICHEL (Contemporary, School of Paris)

> HUTS IN THE WOODS
> canvas 32×25¾, *signed* l.l.: Kikoïne

KLEINHOLZ, FRANK

> CITY CARNIVAL
> canvas 20×24, *signed* l.l.: F. Kleinholz

KNEE, GINA

> SEEDS AND ROOTS
> gouache 18¼×16, *signed* l.r.: Gina Knee '43

> A WALK IN THE RAIN
> watercolor 17½×21½, *signed* l.r.: Gina Knee

KNOOP, GUITOU (French-American Contemporary)

> HEAD OF KATHARINE CORNELL
> bronze 12½ in. high, *signed* rear l.l.: Guitou Knoop '37

KUHLMAN, WALTER

> STREET SCENE
> canvas 18¼×24, *signed* l.r.: Walter Kuhlman 1938

LAITTRE, ELEANOR DE

> FACE CARDS
> canvas 13×22, *signed* l.r.: E. de Laittre 1942

LANE, BETTY

> ST. PETER'S SQUARE
> canvas 16×20, *signed* l.l.: Lane 37

LAUGHLIN, CLARENCE J.

PORTFOLIO OF 23 PHOTOGRAPHS

LAWRENCE, JACOB

30 PANELS FROM "THE MIGRATION OF THE NEGRO"

See Plate 257

masonite panels each 12×18, odd-numbered panels from the complete set of 60, *unsigned*
References: Fortune, November 1941 "And the Migrants Kept Coming", pp. 102–09, 26 illus. in color
Exhibited: Museum of Modern Art, 1942, and Traveling Exh., 1942–44; Ohio State Museum, Columbus, 1945

LAZZARI, PIETRO

GOTHIC STILL LIFE
cardboard panel 25×15, *painted* 1943, *signed* l.c.: Pietro Lazzari

LEE, DORIS

ILLINOIS RIVER TOWN
canvas 32×50, *signed* l.r.: Doris Lee

LEVINE, JACK

THE END OF THE LINE
canvas 36×24, *signed* l.r.: J. Levine

LOGASA, CHARLES (American, 1883–1936)

RAKING LEAVES
canvas 30×36, *unsigned*

LUTZ, DAN

MAIN STREET
watercolor 13½×21¼, *signed* l.r.: Dan Lutz 40

LYMAN, MARY ELIZABETH

SKYLINE DRIVE
watercolor $13\frac{1}{2} \times 19\frac{1}{2}$, *signed* l.l.: M. E. Partridge '37

MacIVER, LOREN

THE WINDOW SHADE
canvas 43×29, *signed* u.l.: MacIver

MARIL, HERMAN

COAL
canvas board 18×24, *signed* l.l.: Herman Maril '35

BALTIMORE WATERFRONT
canvas $14 \times 22\frac{1}{4}$, *signed* l.l.: Herman Maril '34

Plate 252a

PROVINCETOWN
gouache 6×10, *signed* l.l.: Herman Maril

THE ROAD
gouache $10\frac{1}{4} \times 17\frac{1}{4}$, *painted* 1948, *signed* l.r.c.: Herman Maril

STREET CORNER
canvas board 12×18, *signed* l.l.: Herman Maril 49

WOMAN SEWING
cardboard panel $11\frac{1}{4} \times 8\frac{1}{4}$, *painted* 1938, *signed* l.r.: Herman Maril

MAURER, LEONARD

THE HUNTER
canvas 30×24, *signed* l.r.: Leonard Maurer 48

McADAMS, ALFRED

WHO LIVES HERE?
gouache and ink $29\frac{3}{4} \times 19\frac{5}{8}$, *painted c.* 1950, *signed* l.l.: Alf. Mc.

McLAUGHLIN, JAMES*

ANEMONES
masonite panel 29¼×20¾, *painted* 1951, *unsigned*

Plate 255a

THE BARN
canvas 12×16, *painted* 1940, *unsigned*

BOWL AND FLOWERS
canvas 8×14, *painted* 1940, *unsigned*

CORNFLOWERS AND GREEN VASE
gouache on cardboard 11¼×6¾, *painted* 1942, *unsigned*

DUCK DECOY
canvas 10×18, *painted* 1941, *unsigned*

GLASS, FISH AND PLATE
masonite panel 12½×21⅜, *unsigned*

NASTURTIUMS
masonite panel 18×14⅜, *painted* 1949, *unsigned*

THE ROUND TABLE
masonite panel 29½×18⅞, *painted* 1947, *unsigned*

THE SHEPHERD
canvas 28×36, *painted* 1947, *unsigned*

WINDOW SHELVES
canvas 27×20, *painted* 1943, *unsigned*

MEYEROWITZ, WILLIAM

FRUIT AND FLOWERS
canvas 20×24, *signed* l.r.c.: Wm. Meyerowitz

MILLIGAN, GLADYS

STILL LIFE
canvas 18×24, *painted* 1948, *unsigned*

128

MOLLER, HANS (German-American Contemporary)

> *DON QUIXOTE*
> canvas 36×47, *signed* l.r. side: Moller 46

MORRIS, GEORGE L. K.

> *HERALDIC ABSTRACTION*
> canvas 12×16, *signed* l.r.: Morris 42

NEGULESCO, JEAN (Roumanian-American Contemporary)

> *HOUSE IN THE OLIVE TREES*
> composition panel $10\frac{3}{4}×13\frac{3}{4}$, *unsigned*

> *ROUMANIAN STILL LIFE*
> composition panel $15×24\frac{3}{4}$, *signed* l.l.: J. Negulesco 26

NOLAND, KENNETH

> *INSIDE*
> masonite panel $23\frac{1}{8}×29\frac{1}{8}$, *painted c.* 1950, *unsigned*

OBERTEUFFER, HENRIETTE

> *THE CRYSTAL PITCHER*
> canvas 16×20, *signed* u.l.: H. Henriette Oberteuffer

ORR, ELLIOTT

> *THE BLESSING*
> gouache $9\frac{3}{4}×7\frac{1}{2}$, *painted* 1940, *signed* l.r.: Elliot Orr

PACH, WALTER

> *STILL LIFE*
> canvas 16×20, *signed* u.l.: Walter Pach 1928

PEPLOE, SAMUEL JOHN (Scotch 1871-1935)

IONA
wood panel 14¾×17¾, *unsigned*

PEREIRA, I. RICE

TRANSVERSION
Plate 242

oil on masonite panel, and ceramic fluid and porcelain cement on 2 corru-gated glass panels, superimposed, 13½×15¾, *signed* l.r.: I. Rice Pereira '46
Exhibited: Galerie Georges Giroux, Brussels, Exh. of Contemporary American Art, 1948

PERLMUTTER, JACK

ENTERING THE SUBWAY
canvas 22×28, *painted* 1946, *signed* l.r.; Jack Perlmutter

STILL LIFE WITH CHEESE BOX
masonite panel 24×20, *signed* l.r.: Jack Perlmutter

PHILLIPS, LAUGHLIN

FLARE
canvas 18×14, *painted* 1947, *unsigned*

NAUTICAL
Plate 241

masonite panel 24×29, *unsigned*

PIPER, JOHN (English Contemporary)*

BOLSOVER CASTLE
watercolor with ink 15⅛×20½, *painted* 1947, *signed* l.r.: John Piper

THE CHURCH
canvas mounted on wood 6×7⅞, *signed* l.r.: John Piper

LLYN BOCHLWYD
watercolor with ink $14\frac{1}{4}\times20\frac{3}{8}$, *painted* 1947, *signed* l.r.: John Piper

OCKHAM MONUMENT
gouache with ink and lithographic crayon, $19\frac{3}{4}\times25$, *painted* 1946–47

RUSSELL MONUMENTS AT STRENSHAM   Plate 228
composition panel 30×25, *painted c.* 1945–46, *signed* l.r.: John Piper

STONE GATE, PORTLAND   Plate 229
canvas 36×48, *painted* 1950, *signed* l.r.: John Piper

THUNDERSTORM
wood panel $5\frac{7}{8}\times8$, *signed* l.l.: John Piper

WALL AT MUCHELNEY ABBEY
canvas mounted on wood 20×24, *painted* 1941, *signed* l.r.: John Piper

POISSON, LOUVERTURE (Haitian Contemporary)

LANDSCAPE WITH PALMS
(Gift of Selden Rodman)
oil on cardboard $11\times14\frac{1}{8}$, *signed* l.r.c.: Louverture Poisson F/6/45

PORTER, LOUIS H.

THE CITY
masonite panel $24\times19\frac{3}{4}$, *painted* 1948, *signed* l.r.: Porter

PRESTOPINO, GREGORIO

WATERFRONT, NEW YORK
watercolor 18×24, *signed* l.r.: Prestopino

RANDALL, BYRON

NOCTURNE
watercolor $21\frac{1}{2}\times30$, *unsigned*

ROSENBERG, JAMES N.

ADIRONDACKS
canvas 25×30, *signed* l.l.: J N R '44

ROSENBERG, NELSON

THE ROAD
watercolor 14½×22, *painted* 1937, *signed* l.r.: N. Rosenberg

ROSENBORG, RALPH

ASCENDING
gouache 9¼×12½, *signed* l.l.: Rosenborg

ROSENFELD, EDWARD

CABIN INTERIOR
masonite panel 9×11, *painted* 1936, *signed* l.l.: Edward Rosenfeld

KITCHEN SINK   *Plate 255b*
masonite panel 21½×17½, *signed* u.r.c.: Edward Rosenfeld 35

THE SCULPTOR'S STUDIO
masonite panel 18×30¼, *painted* 1944, *signed* l.l.: Edward Rosenfeld

SHORE KITCHEN
masonite panel 25×35, *signed* l.l.: Rosenfeld 40

STREET IN BALTIMORE
masonite panel 22×28, *painted* 1941, *unsigned*

RUELLAN, ANDRÉE

THE WIND-UP
canvas 20×30, *painted c.* 1941, *signed* l.l.: Andrée Ruellan

RUSH, OLIVE

CHARROS AT RODEO
watercolor $13\frac{1}{2} \times 16\frac{1}{2}$, *signed* l.r.: Rush 1929

SANDS, ETHEL (English Contemporary)

SUNLIT ROOM
canvas 20×24, *signed* l.r.: Sands

SARGENT, RICHARD

SUMMERVILLE, S. C.
watercolor $11 \times 17\frac{1}{2}$, *signed* l.l.: Sargent

TWO KEY WEST HOUSES
watercolor $10\frac{1}{2} \times 15\frac{1}{4}$, *signed* l.r.: Sargent

WAREHOUSES
watercolor $8\frac{1}{4} \times 10\frac{1}{4}$, *signed* l.l.: Sargent

SCHALLINGER, MAX (Austrian-American Contemporary)

*FINALE (ALLEGRO MODERATO) FROM THE
"SALZKAMMERGUT" SYMPHONY*
masonite panel 48×48, *unsigned*

SCHANKER, LOUIS

LANDSCAPE THROUGH THE WINDOW
tempera on paper $22\frac{1}{2} \times 31$, *signed* l.r.: Schanker 45

MIDSUMMER LANDSCAPE
tempera on paper $21 \times 29\frac{1}{2}$, *signed* l.r.: Schanker 45

MUSICAL COMPOSITION
color wood-block print $15\frac{1}{8} \times 4\frac{1}{8}$, *signed* l.r.: Schanker

SCHNEIDER, GERARD (French Contemporary)

OPUS 445, 1950
canvas $57\frac{1}{4} \times 38$, *signed* l.r.: Schneider VII 50

SCHULHOFF, WILLIAM

INTERIOR
canvas $21\frac{1}{2} \times 18$, *signed* l.r.: Schulhoff

SCHULTZ, HARRY

MERRY-GO-ROUND
canvas 16×20, *signed* l.l.: H. Schultz 30

SEGY, LADISLAS (Hungarian-American Contemporary)

DARK VILLAGE
masonite panel 16×24, *signed* l.l.: Segy 41

SERNA, ISMAEL GONZALEZ DE LA
(Spanish Contemporary, School of Paris)

FRUIT AND FLOWERS
canvas $39\frac{1}{4} \times 31\frac{3}{4}$, *signed* (twice) u.l.: G. de la Serna, Paris 26, and l.l.
part of picture: I. G. de la S.

SMITH, VERN

OWLS
canvas 20×16, *painted* 1950, *signed* u.l.: Vern

SOLMAN, JOSEPH

BOOKS AND PRINT
composition panel 12×20, *painted* 1947, *signed* l.l. side: J.S.

PORTRAIT OF MURRAY
canvas board panel $11\frac{1}{2}\times17\frac{1}{2}$, *signed* l.l.c.: J.S.

THE ROOM
composition panel 16×24, *painted* 1949, *signed* l.r.: J. S.

SOPHER, AARON

ALICE ANNA STREET
ink wash and pen drawing $7\frac{3}{4}\times6\frac{7}{8}$, *signed* l.r.c.: A. Sopher

BABY CARRIAGE
watercolor and ink drawing $4\frac{3}{4}\times6$, *signed* l.r.: A. Sopher

CHEER CENTER
ink wash and pen drawing $4\frac{7}{8}\times4\frac{7}{8}$, *signed* l.l.c.: A. Sopher '34

SOULAGES, PIERRE (French Contemporary)

JULY 10, 1950   *Plate 256*
canvas $51\frac{1}{4}\times63\frac{3}{4}$, *signed* l.l.: Soulages 10.7.50

SOUVERBIE, JEAN (French Contemporary)

CARD PLAYERS
canvas $19\frac{1}{2}\times25\frac{1}{2}$, *signed* l.l.: Souverbie 26

SOYER, MOSES

OLD MAN
wood panel 15×10, *signed* l.r.: M. Soyer

SOYER, RAPHAEL

SELF PORTRAIT
wood panel $11\times8\frac{1}{4}$, *signed* l.l.: Raphael Soyer

SPRUCE, EVERETT

ARKANSAS LANDSCAPE
masonite panel 21¼×25, *signed* l.l.: E. Spruce '38

DE STAËL, NICOLAS (French Contemporary)

NORTH
canvas 9½×16¼, *signed* l.r.: Staël

STAMOS, THEODOROS*

FOUNTAIN
watercolor 24¼×18¾, *signed*: Stamos 49

MOSSES
gouache 11½×17½, *signed* l.l.: Stamos 49

MOON CHALICE
masonite panel 39¾×24½, *signed* l.l.c.: T. Stamos '49

THE SACRIFICE OF CHRONOS, No. 2
masonite panel 48×36, *signed* l.l.: T. Stamos '48

WORLD TABLET   *Plate 247*
masonite panel 48×36, *signed* l.l.: T. Stamos '48

SUTHERLAND, GRAHAM (English Contemporary)

VINE PERGOLA   *Plate 231*
canvas 13×16, *signed* on back: Sutherland 1947

TAMAYO, RUFINO (Mexican Contemporary)

CARNIVAL
canvas 43×33, *signed* l.l.: Tamayo 41
Exhibited: Instituto Nacional de Bellas Artes, Mexico City, Tamayo Exh.
1948, no. 26, illus. in cat.

MANDOLINS AND PINEAPPLES
canvas 19¾×27½, *signed* l.l.: Tamayo 30

TAYLOR, PRENTISS

LOUISBURG SQUARE
lithograph 14×9¾, *signed* l.r.: Prentiss Taylor, April 1933, and on plate
l.l.: PT XXVII

SAINT HELENA'S, BEAUFORT
lithograph 14×11, *signed* l.r.: Prentiss Taylor, May 1934, and on plate
l.l.: PT XXXVIII

SUPPER IN PORT
lithograph 10×13, *signed* l.r.: Prentiss Taylor, November 1937, and on
plate l.l.: PT. LIII

TOLEGIAN, MANUEL

TURKEY IN THE STRAW
masonite panel 24×32, *signed* l.l.: Tolegian 37

TOMLIN, BRADLEY WALKER

THE GOBLET   *Plate 240*
canvas 22×29, *signed* u.r.: Tomlin 1940

TOWNSEND, LEE

STARTING BEFORE THE SHOWER
canvas 23½×29, *signed* l.r.: Lee Townsend

VARIAN, DOROTHY

RED PLUMS AND MELON
canvas 18×27, *signed* l.l.: D. Varian

WALKER, ROBERT

> *BEFORE A STORM*
> canvas 26×20¼, *signed* l.l.: R. Walker

WALKER, STEPHEN

> *HOME-GROWN*
> canvas 20×24, *painted* 1936, *signed* u.l.: S. Walker

> *TOOL SHED*
> wood panel 35½×51½, *signed* l.r.: Stephen Walker

WATKINS, MARY BRADLEY

> *THE BLUE AND THE STRAWBERRY ROAN*   *Plate 248b*
> canvas 8×16, *painted* 1939, *unsigned*

> *MOUNTAIN AND PINE*
> canvas 18×14, *painted* 1950, *unsigned*

> *THE SEASONS*
> canvas 16×20, *painted* 1950, *unsigned*

> *SHOWERS*
> canvas 18×27, *painted* 1939, *unsigned*

WELLS, JAMES LESESNE

> *JOURNEY TO EGYPT*
> composition panel 13½×16, *unsigned*

WHITAKER, LAWRENCE

> *NIGHT SHIFT*
> canvas 20¾×26, *signed* l.r.: Lawrence Whitaker

WIEGHARDT, PAUL (German-American Contemporary)

> *COUNTY FAIR*
> watercolor 16¼×22⅛, *signed* l.r.: P. Wieghardt 1942

> *TERRACE*
> watercolor 18⅝×26, *signed* l.r.: P. Wieghardt 1942

WUTHENAU, A. VON

> *PASTORAL*
> canvas 12×20, *unsigned*

XCÉRON, JEAN (Greek-American Contemporary)

> *THE VILLAGE*
> canvas 21¼×25½, *signed* u.r.: J. Xcéron 27

YASHIMA, TARO (Japanese-American Contemporary)

> *GREEN FIELDS AND BUILDING*
> canvas 25×30, *signed* l.l.: Yashima, July 1950

ZERBE, KARL (German-American Contemporary)

> *PARK STREET, BOSTON*   *Plate 230*
> encaustic on canvas 30×36, *painted* 1942, *signed* l.l.: Zerbe
> *Exhibited:* Tate Gallery, London, Exhibition of American Paintings,
> 1946

> *WASHINGTON SQUARE, CHARLESTON*
> gouache 17½×25, *painted* 1940, *signed* l.l. side: Zerbe

ZEREGA, ANDREA

> *STORMING*
> canvas 16×20, *signed* l.l.: Zerega 43

SOME RECENT ACQUISITIONS

GAUGUIN, PAUL

STILL LIFE WITH HAM (Le Jambon)   *Plate 258*
canvas $19\frac{3}{4} \times 22\frac{3}{4}$, *painted* 1889, *signed* l.r.c. (on tablecloth): P. Go
Collections: A. Vollard, Paris; Maurice Cortot

FRAGMENT COPTIC TAPESTRY   *Plate 259a*

5–6th century A.D.
Collections: Kelekian

VAUGHAN, KEITH

YORKSHIRE FARM HOUSE   *Plate 259b*
watercolor $11 \times 14\frac{1}{2}$, *signed* l.r.: Keith Vaughan 1945

PHILLIPS, MARJORIE

NIGHT BASEBALL   *Plate 260*
canvas 24×36, *painted* 1951, *signed* l.l.: Marjorie Phillips

The illustrations which follow represent a significant cross-section of the Collection. Many of our important paintings are not illustrated while a few of those selected for reproduction are included because they are by artists on the staff of the Gallery or closely affiliated with it. Thus we frankly acknowledge the essentially intimate character of the Collection and of its personal associations.

D. P.

HONORÉ DAUMIER   Two Sculptors

PIERRE AUGUSTE RENOIR

The Luncheon of the Boating Party

Street Pavers

VINCENT VAN GOGH

PAUL CÉZANNE   Seated Woman in Blue

EDGAR DEGAS

Dancers at the Bar

PIERRE BONNARD   Woman and Dog

GEORGES ROUAULT   Verlaine

GEORGES BRAQUE   The Round Table

1 GIORGIONE.(?)   The Hour Glass

2 ANTONIO TRAVI

3 EL GRECO (DOMENIKOS THEOTOKOPOULOS)   The Repentant Peter

4a FRANCESCO GUARDI   Piazza San Marco

4b WILLIAM HOGARTH   The Singing Party

The Shipwreck

6 FRANCISCO JOSÉ DE GOYA Y LUCIENTES   The Repentant Peter

7 JEAN BAPTISTE SIMÉON CHARDIN   A Bowl of Plums

8 JEAN HONORÉ FRAGONARD   Rodomonte Leaps across the Moat

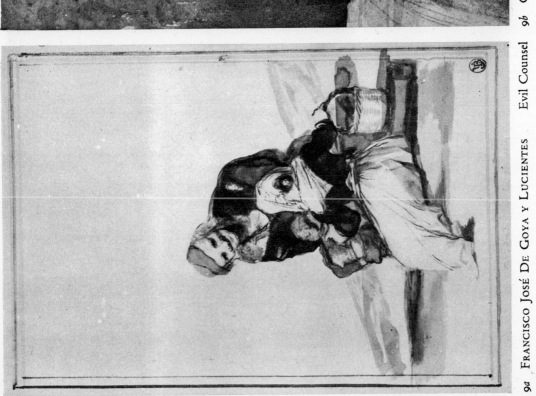

9a Francisco José De Goya y Lucientes   Evil Counsel   9b Constantin Guys   Young Spanish Girl

10a JOSEPH MALLORD WILLIAM TURNER   Coast Scene with Sails

10b JOHN CONSTABLE   English Landscape

11 JOHN CONSTABLE

On the River Stour

13   I. J. H. BRADLEY

The 'Cellist

14   Jean Auguste Dominique Ingres   The Bather

15*a* JEAN BAPTISTE CAMILLE COROT   View from the Farnese Gardens, Rome

15*b* JEAN BAPTISTE CAMILLE COROT   Civita Castellana, Plains and Mountains

16 Eugène Delacroix   Paganini

Horses Coming Out of the Sea

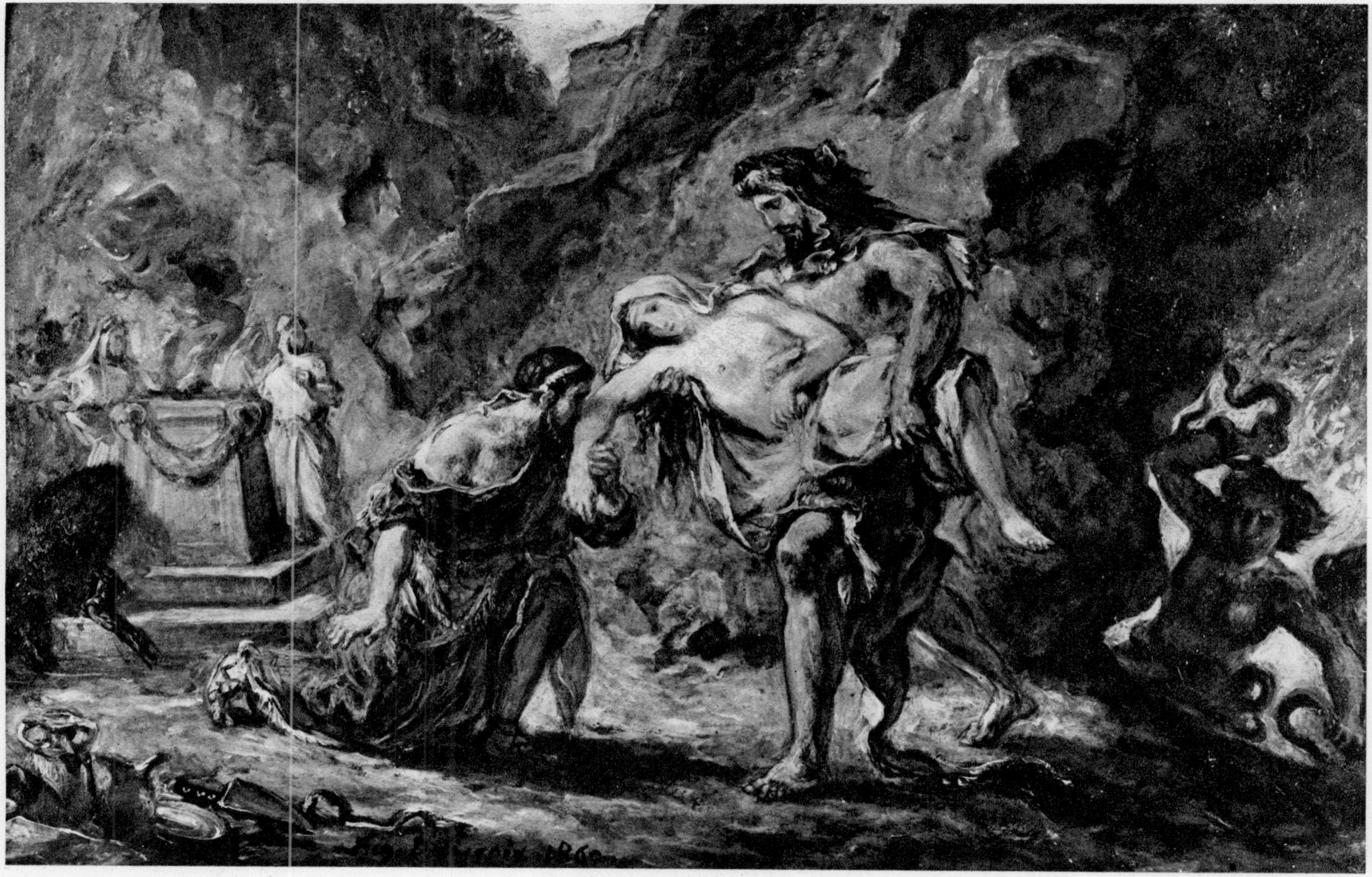

19 EUGÈNE DELACROIX — Hercules and Alcestis

20 HONORÉ DAUMIER   On a Bridge at Night

21 HONORÉ DAUMIER   To the Street

22 Honoré Daumier

23 HONORÉ DAUMIER   The Painter at his Easel

24 Honoré Daumier

25 HONORÉ DAUMIER   Three Lawyers

Two Sculptors

29 JEAN BAPTISTE CARPEAUX   Street Scene

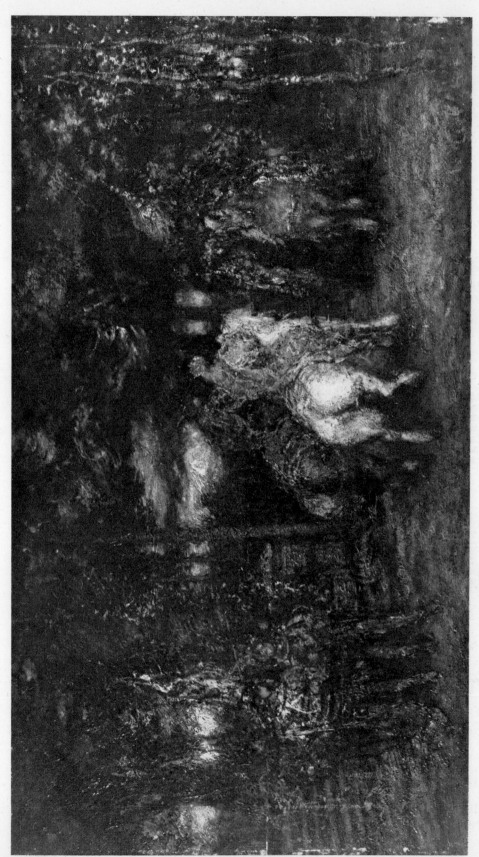

31   Adolphe Monticelli

32 JEAN BAPTISTE CAMILLE COROT   Portrait of a Woman

Dairy Farm

The Mediterranean

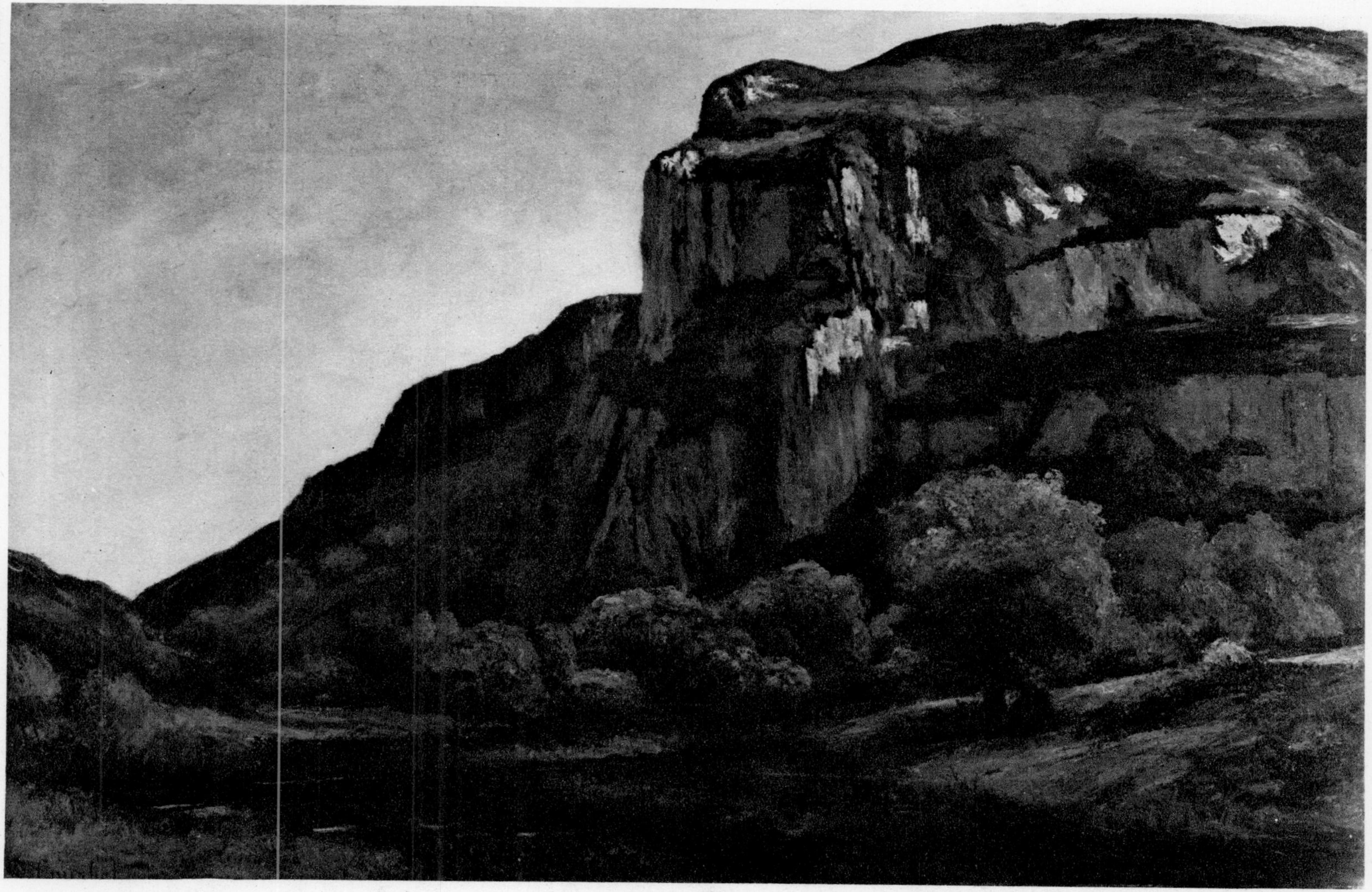

35 Gustave Courbet — Rocks at Ornans

Greek Colony, Massilia

PIERRE PUVIS DE CHAVANNES

Marseilles, Port of the Orient

38a EUGÈNE LOUIS BOUDIN   Beach at Trouville

38b HENRI FANTIN-LATOUR   Manet in his Studio

Lake Albano

Moonlight, Tarpon Springs

42 GEORGE FULLER   Ideal Head

43 JAMES ABBOTT McNEILL WHISTLER   Miss Lillian Woakes

44   WINSLOW HOMER

45a WINSLOW HOMER   Rowing Home

45b ALBERT PINKHAM RYDER   Homeward Bound

46a ALBERT PINKHAM RYDER   Dead Bird

46b ALBERT PINKHAM RYDER   Gay Head

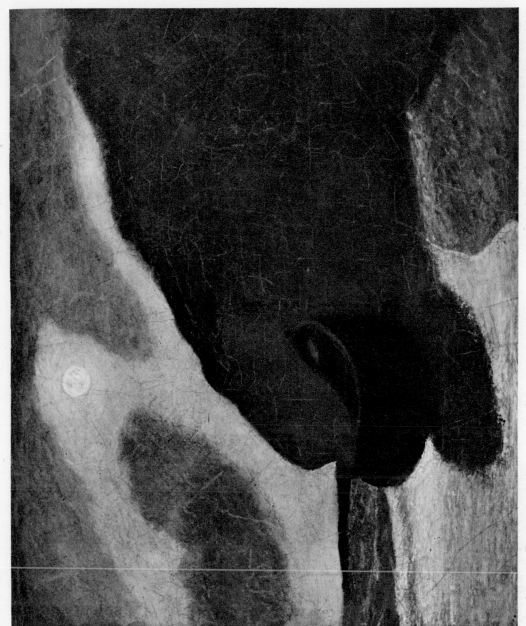

47 ALBERT PINKHAM RYDER

Moonlit Cove

48 ALBERT PINKHAM RYDER   Desdemona

Fishermen's Huts

50 ALBERT PINKHAM RYDER   Resurrection

Macbeth and the Witches

53 THOMAS EAKINS   Miss Van Buren

54 ALFRED SISLEY   ·   Snow at Louveciennes

55 BERTHE MORISOT   Two Girls

59 EDGAR DEGAS   Dancers at the Bar

After the Bath

61 ODILON REDON   Mystery

The Road to Vetheuil

63 PIERRE AUGUSTE RENOIR

Entrance to the Public Gardens at Arles

65   Vincent van Gogh

Fields at Bellevue

68 PAUL CÉZANNE   Self Portrait

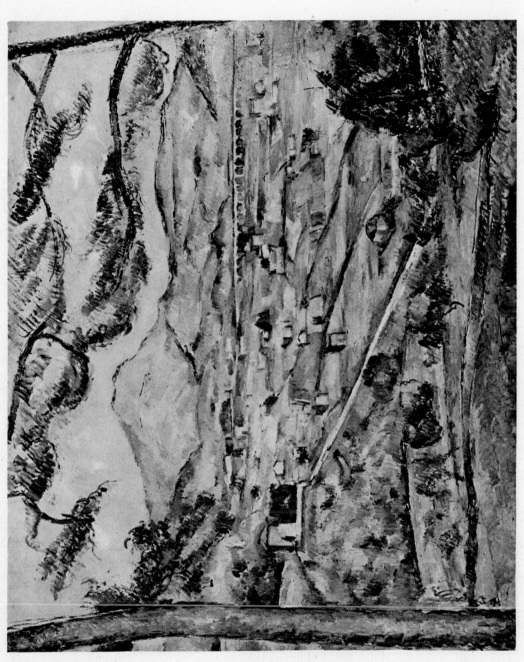

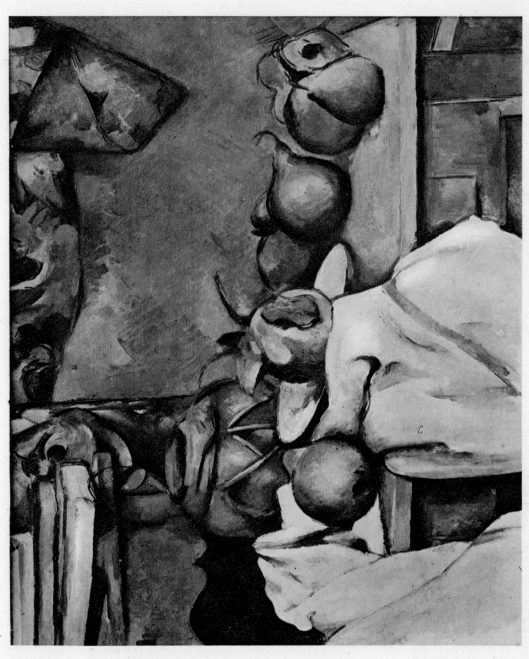

70 PAUL CÉZANNE

Pomegranate and Pears (gift of Gifford Phillips)

71 PAUL CÉZANNE   Seated Woman in Blue

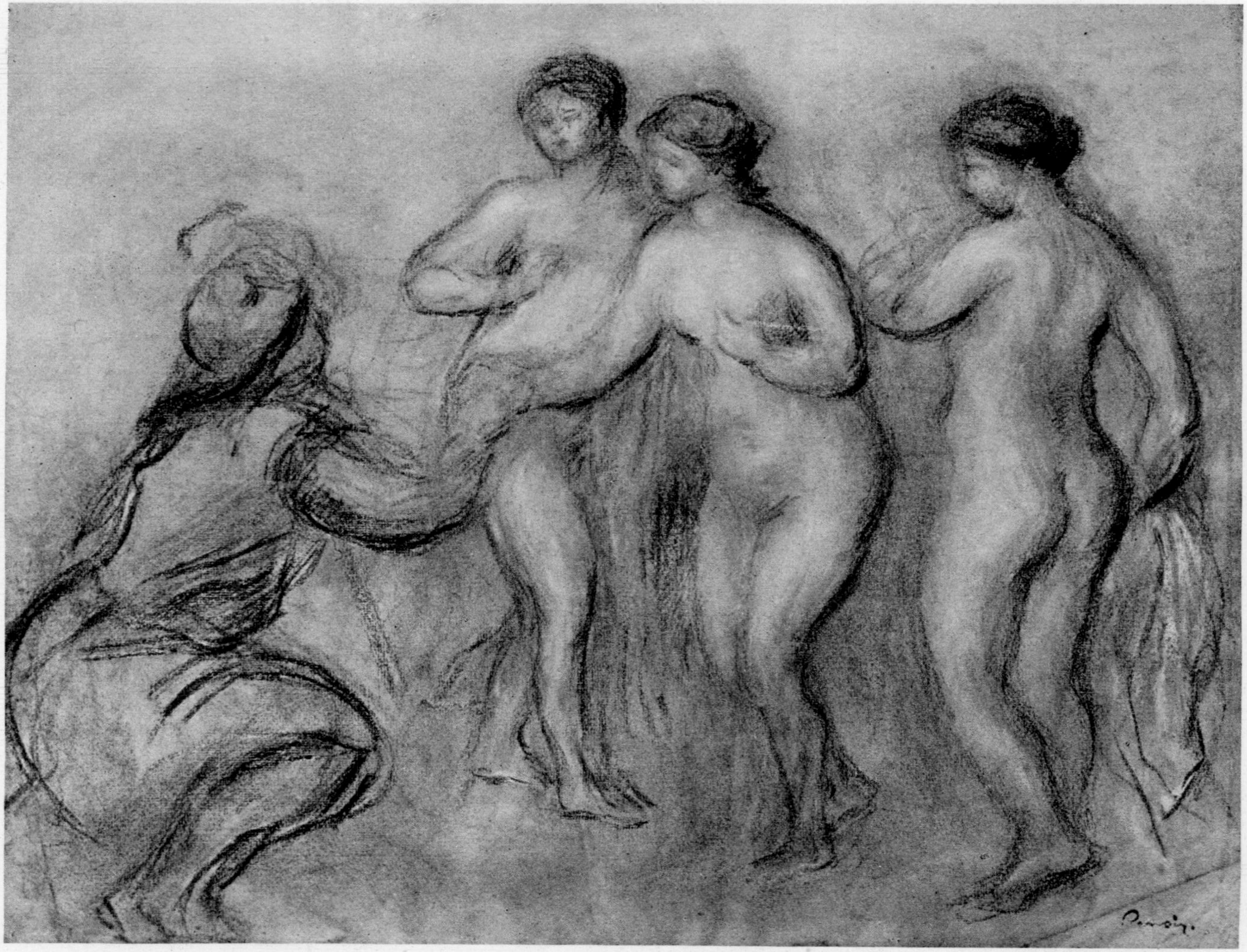

72 Pierre Auguste Renoir — The Judgment of Paris

ALBERT ANDRÉ   Renoir in his Studio at Cagnes

74   Georges Pierre Seurat   First Drawing for "The Side Show"

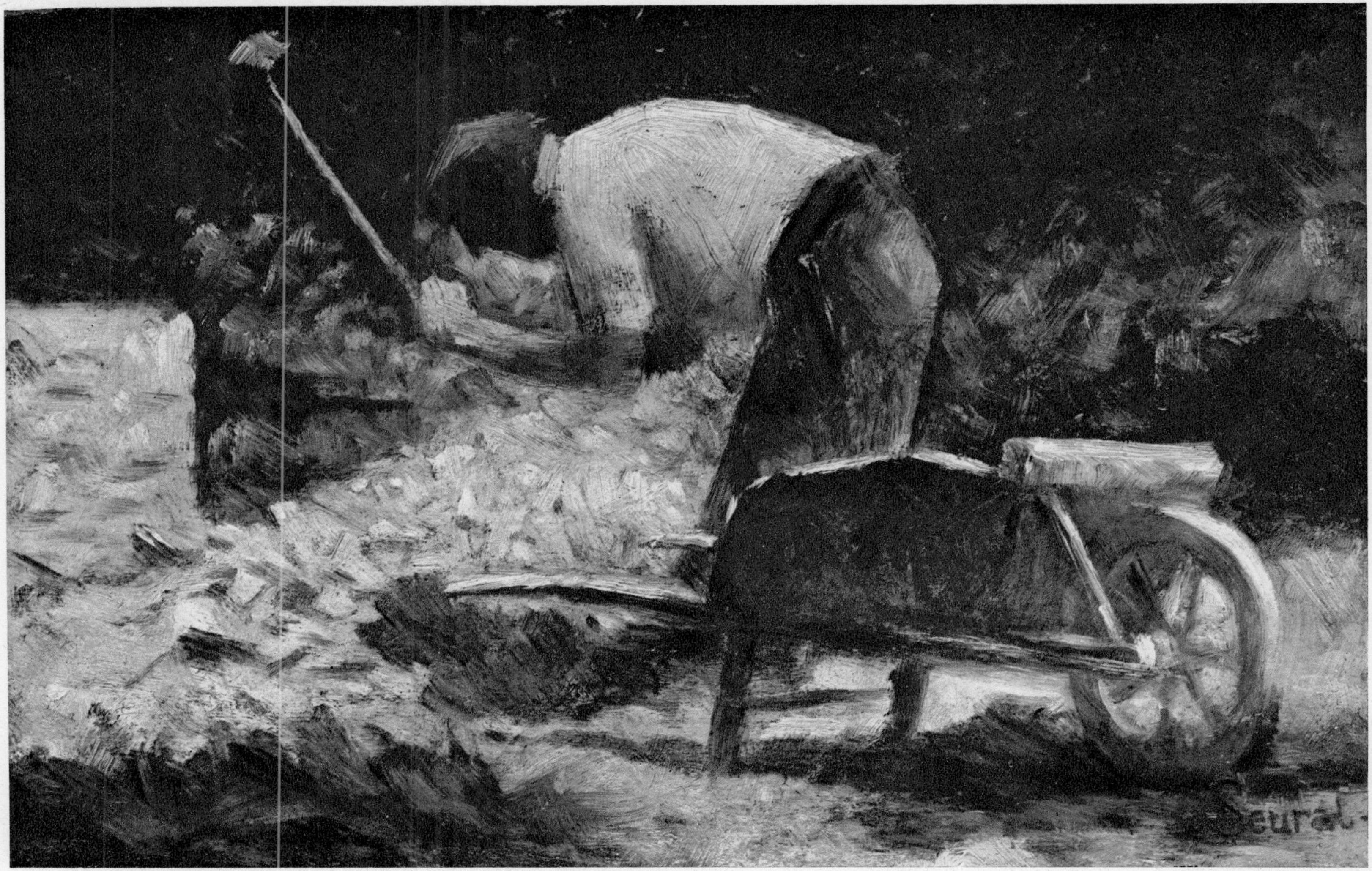

75 GEORGES PIERRE SEURAT The Stone Breaker

76 John H. Twachtman

77 JOHN H. TWACHTMAN   Emerald Pool

78 JULIAN ALDEN WEIR   Pan and the Wolf

79 Julian Alden Weir

80 WALTER RICHARD SICKERT   Portrait of Fred Winter

81 CHILDE HASSAM   Washington Arch, Spring

Afternoon, Pincian Hill

83 MAURICE PRENDERGAST   Ponte della Paglia

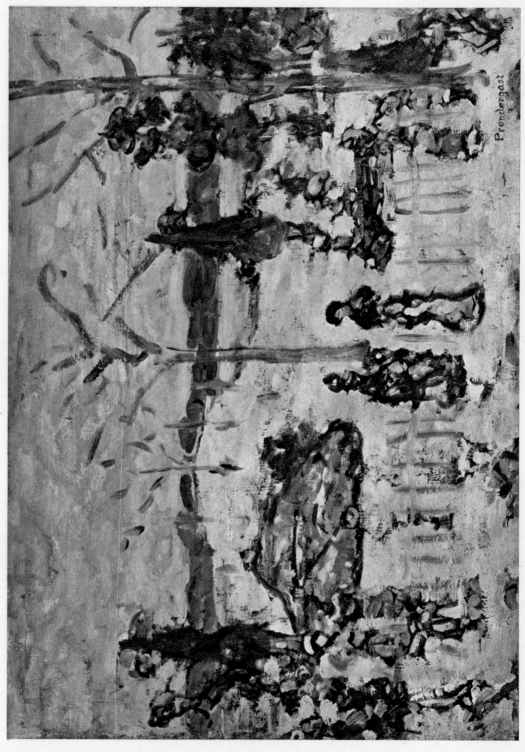

Prendergast

85 Maurice Prendergast

Along the Erie Canal

87a   ARTHUR B. DAVIES   Springtime of Delight

87b   ARTHUR B. DAVIES   The Flood

88 HENRI ROUSSEAU (Le Douanier) Notre Dame

Yuma, Arizona

90 Louis Eilshemius   Balcony View

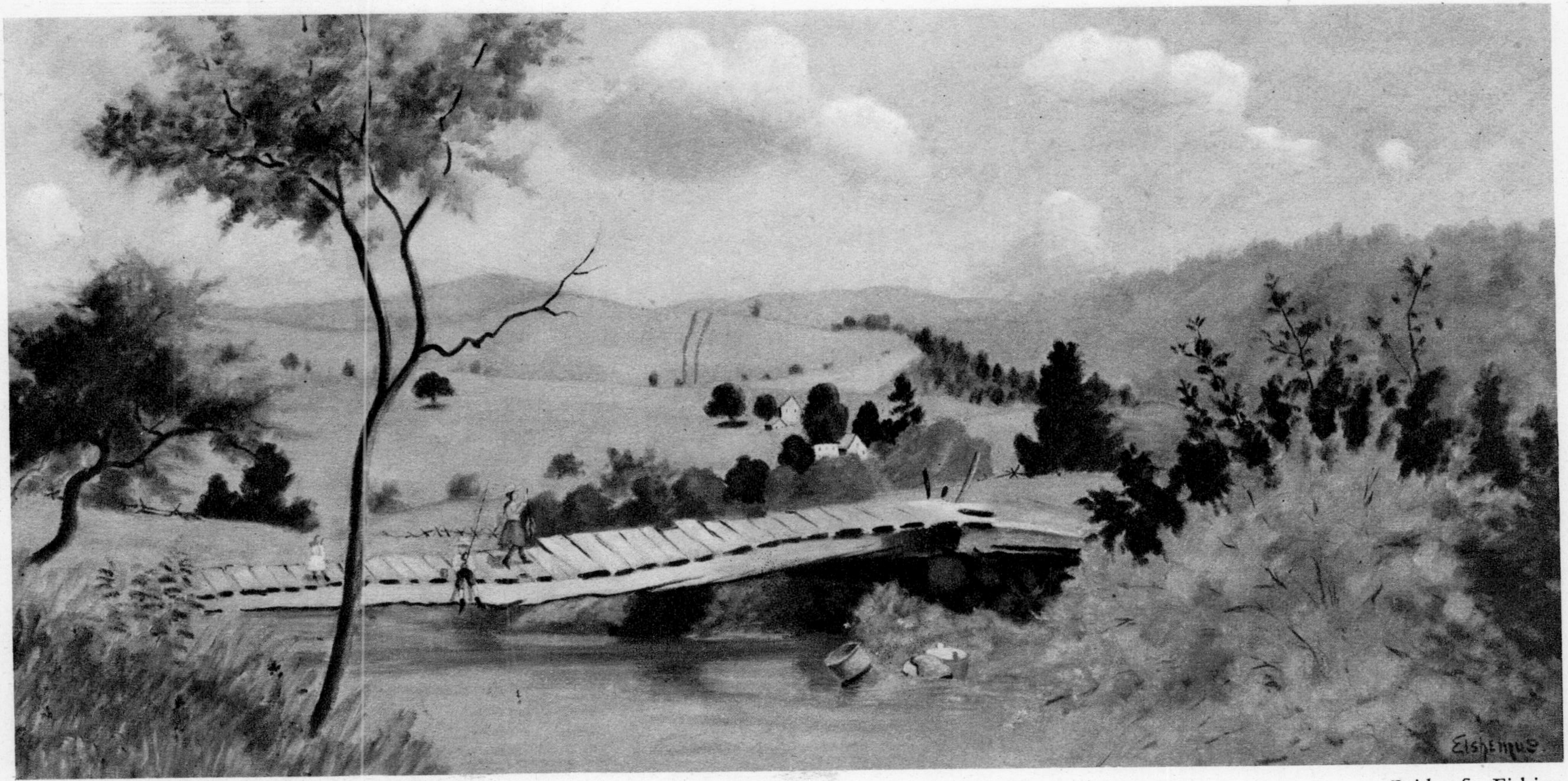

91 Louis Eilshemius

Bridge for Fishing

92 LOUIS EILSHEMIUS   Madge in the Morning

Cabs for Hire

95 WALTER RICHARD SICKERT   Victoria and Melbourne

Circus Rider

99 ÉDOUARD VUILLARD   Woman Sweeping

Ludovico Magno

101 EDOUARD VUILLARD   Waiting

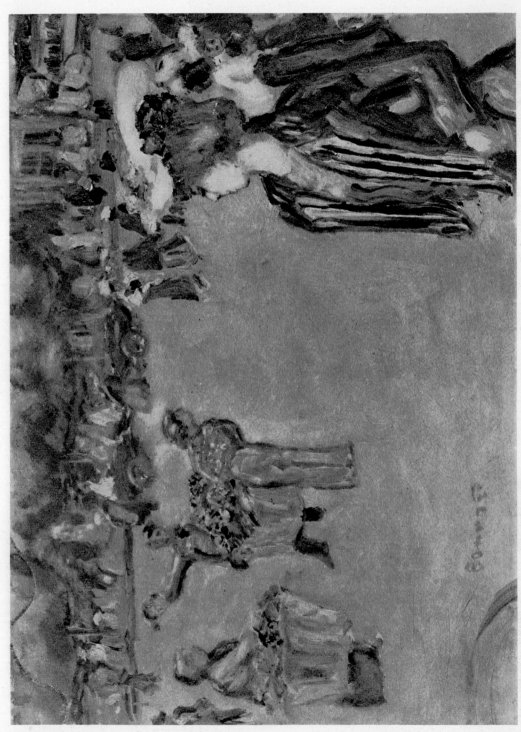

103   K. Xavier Roussel   Faun and Nymph under a Tree

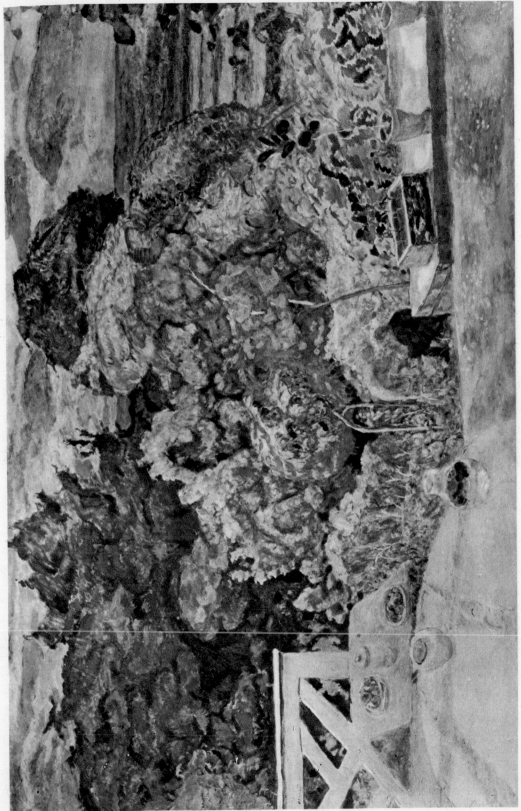

106 PIERRE BONNARD   Woman and Dog

Children and Cat

107 PIERRE BONNARD

The Chequered Table Cover

110 PIERRE BONNARD

The Riviera

111   PIERRE BONNARD   Grape Harvest

112 PIERRE BONNARD   The Palm

113 PIERRE BONNARD   The Open Window

114 GEORGE B. LUKS

Sulking Boy

115   GEORGE B. LUKS   Otis Skinner as Col. Bridau

116 GEORGE B. LUKS   Telling Fortunes

The Tambourine

118 ERNEST LAWSON

Spring Night, Harlem River

119 ERNEST LAWSON

May in the Mountains

121 ERNEST LAWSON   After Rain

122 JOHN SLOAN

The Wake of the Ferry

123 JOHN SLOAN   Old Clown Making Up

124 Augustus Vincent Tack   Passacaglia

125 AUGUSTUS VINCENT TACK   The Voice of Many Waters

126 Augustus Vincent Tack

Aspiration

128 JOHN MARIN

Maine Islands

129 JOHN MARIN

130 JOHN MARIN

Back of Bear Mountain

Four-Master Off the Cape

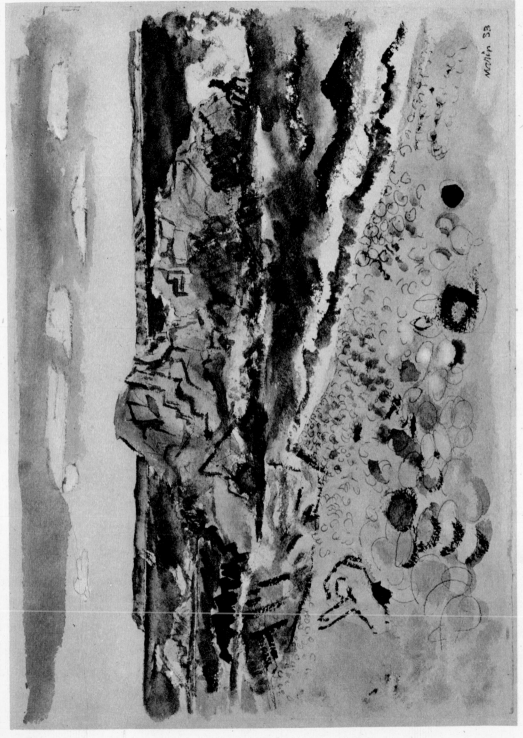

133   JOHN MARIN   Quoddy Head, Maine Coast

134   JOHN MARIN

Fifth Avenue at Forty-second Street

135 JOHN MARIN

Bryant Square

136 JOHN MARIN

Tunk Mountains, Autumn, Maine

137 ALFRED H. MAURER

138 HENRI MATISSE   Studio, Quai St. Michel

139 HENRI MATISSE   Interior with Egyptian Curtain

140 GEORGES ROUAULT   Christ and the High Priest

141a GEORGES ROUAULT   Still Waters

141b GEORGES ROUAULT   Afterglow, Galilee

143 GEORGES ROUAULT   Verlaine

144 PIET MONDRIAN   Square Composition

145a JACQUES VILLON   The Grain Does Not Die

145b JACQUES VILLON   The Little Machine Shop

146 PAUL KLEE   Actor of the Oriental Theatre

147   WASSILY KANDINSKY   Autumn

148a PAUL KLEE   Arrival of the Circus

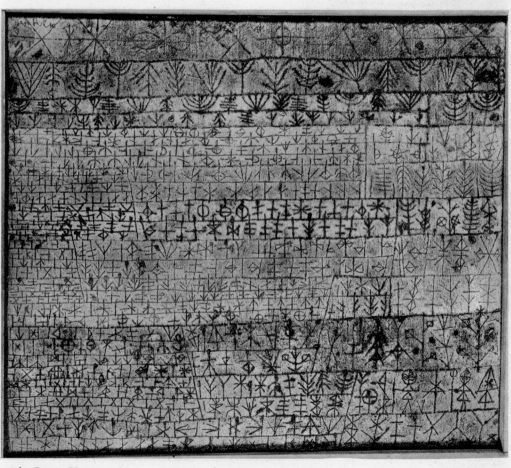

148b PAUL KLEE   Tree Nursery

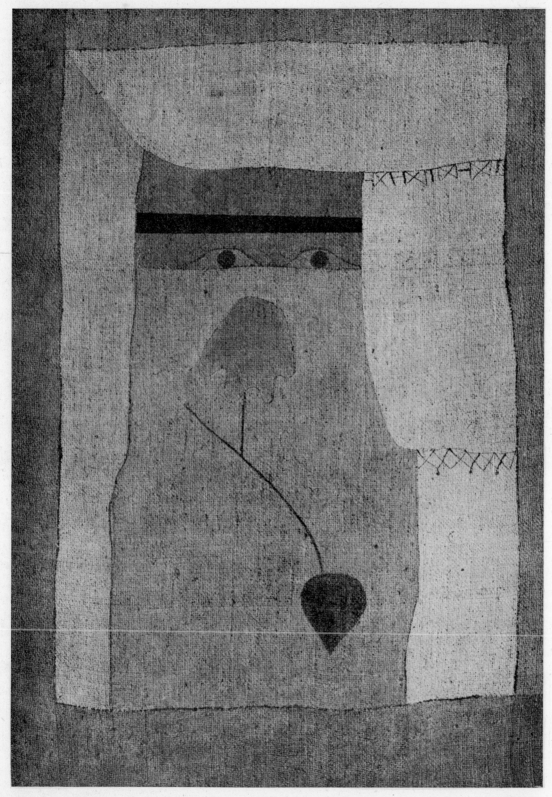

149 PAUL KLEE   Arab Song

150 PAUL KLEE   Botanical Laboratory

151   PAUL KLEE   Picture Album

152 ARISTIDE MAILLOL   Head of a Woman

153   CHARLES DESPIAU   Head of Mme Derain

154a RAOUL DUFY   Joinville

154b RAOUL DUFY   Château and Horses

155 RAOUL DUFY

Versailles

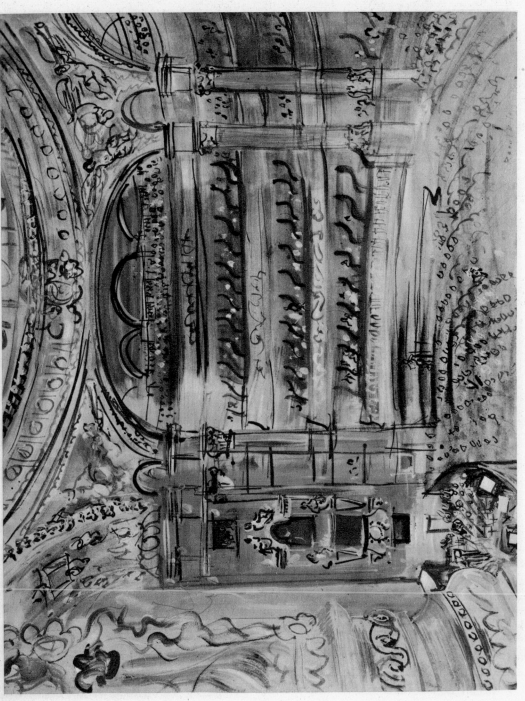

157   RAOUL DUFY   The Opera, Paris

158 JUAN GRIS   Still Life with Newspaper

159a JUAN GRIS   Abstraction

159b JUAN GRIS   Bowl and Package of Cigarettes

160 ANDRÉ DERAIN

Decorative Landscape

161 ROGER DE LA FRESNAYE

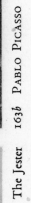

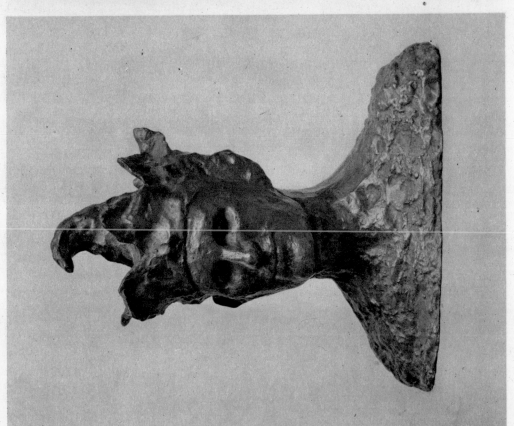

The Jester   163*b*   PABLO PICASSO

163*a*   PABLO PICASSO

164 MAURICE UTRILLO   Abbey of Saint-Denis

165 AMEDEO MODIGLIANI   Elena Pavlowski

166 GEORGE BELLOWS   Emma in Black

167   KENNETH HAYES MILLER   Portrait of Albert P. Ryder

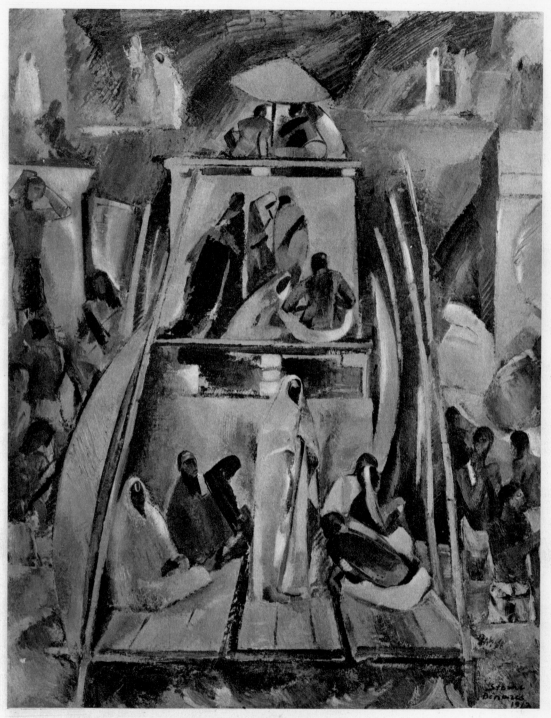

168　Maurice Sterne

Benares

169 MAURICE STERNE   Mother and Child

171 DAVID BURLIUK   At the Inn

1724   CHAIM SOUTINE   Profile   172b   MAX WEBER   Draped Head

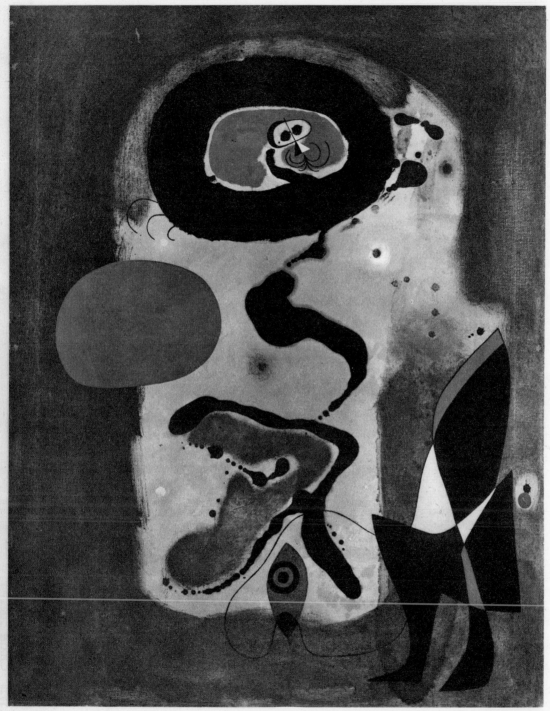

173 JOAN MIRÓ   Red Sun

174a CHAIM SOUTINE   The Return from School

174b CHAIM SOUTINE   Windy Day, Auxerre

175　CHAIM SOUTINE

178a GEORGES BRAQUE   Lemons and Oysters

178b GEORGES BRAQUE   Pitcher, Pipe and Pear

179*a*   GEORGES BRAQUE   Plums, Pears, Nuts and Knife

179*b*   GEORGES BRAQUE   Lemons, Peaches and Compotier

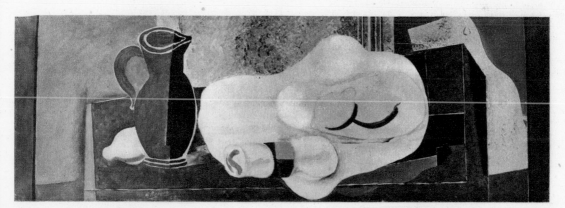

179*c*   GEORGES BRAQUE   Lemons and Napkin Ring

180   GEORGES BRAQUE   The Wash Stand

181 GEORGES BRAQUE   The Round Table

182*a* ANDRÉ DERAIN   A Brunette

182*b* WALT KUHN   Tulip Buds

183 ANDRÉ DERAIN

Southern France

184a ARTHUR G. DOVE   Huntington Harbor

184b MARSDEN HARTLEY   Off to the Banks

185   ARTHUR G. DOVE   Golden Storm

186a ARTHUR G. DOVE   Electric Peach Orchard

186b ARTHUR G. DOVE   Life Goes On

187   MARSDEN HARTLEY

Cows in Pasture

189   ARTHUR G. DOVE   Rise of the Full Moon

190 ARTHUR G. DOVE   Flour Mill Abstraction

191 ARTHUR G. DOVE   Rain or Snow

192a   HORACE PIPPIN   Domino Players

192b   HORACE PIPPIN   Barracks

193*a* ELISABETH POE   Agate Heights

193*b* ARTHUR G. DOVE   Woodpecker

194a   MAURICE STERNE   After Rain

194b   MAX WEBER   After an Ice Storm

195a GIFFORD BEAL   Impression from "Life with Father"

195b GIFFORD BEAL   Circus Ponies

Ship Chandlers' Row

Approaching a City

198a CHARLES DEMUTH   Red Chimneys

198b CHARLES DEMUTH   Egg Plant

199 GEORGIA O'KEEFFE   Dark Red Leaves on White

OSKAR KOKOSCHKA

Portrait of a Cardinal

201 OSKAR KOKOSCHKA   Portrait of Mme Franzos

202 OSKAR KOKOSCHKA

203   OSKAR KOKOSCHKA

204　Georgia O'Keeffe   The White Place in Shadow

Offices

206a ROCKWELL KENT   Burial of a Young Man

206b MILTON AVERY   Harbor at Night

207a PIERRE EUGÈNE CLAIRIN   A Château

207b CHRISTOPHER WOOD   Tiger and Arc de Triomphe

208 KARL KNATHS   Cock and Glove

209 KARL KNATHS   Clam Diggers

210a KARL KNATHS   Frightened Deer in Moonlight

210b KARL KNATHS   Harvest

211*a* KARL KNATHS   Kit and Kin

211*b* KARL KNATHS   Connecticut Clock

212*a* CHARLES BURCHFIELD   Barn

212*b* CHARLES BURCHFIELD   Woman in Doorway

Three Days of Rain

214a PRESTON DICKINSON   Along the River

214b STUART DAVIS   Corner Café

215 MORRIS KANTOR   Union Square, Night

216 FRANKLIN WATKINS   The Angel Will Turn a Page in the Book

217 FRANKLIN WATKINS   Autumn Recollections

218 EUGENE BERMAN   Daybreak

219 EUGENE BERMAN   Courtyard

220 BERNARD KARFIOL   Boy

221 YASUO KUNIYOSHI   Maine Family

222 MARJORIE PHILLIPS   Poppies

223a MARJORIE PHILLIPS   Little Bouquet

223b MARJORIE PHILLIPS   Farm Road

Sun After Rain

225a HAROLD WESTON   Loneliness

225b HAROLD WESTON   The Arena

226 HENRY MOORE   Family Group

227a Ben Nicholson   Still Life (Winter)

227b Henry Moore   Figures in a Setting

228 JOHN PIPER   Russell Monuments at Strensham

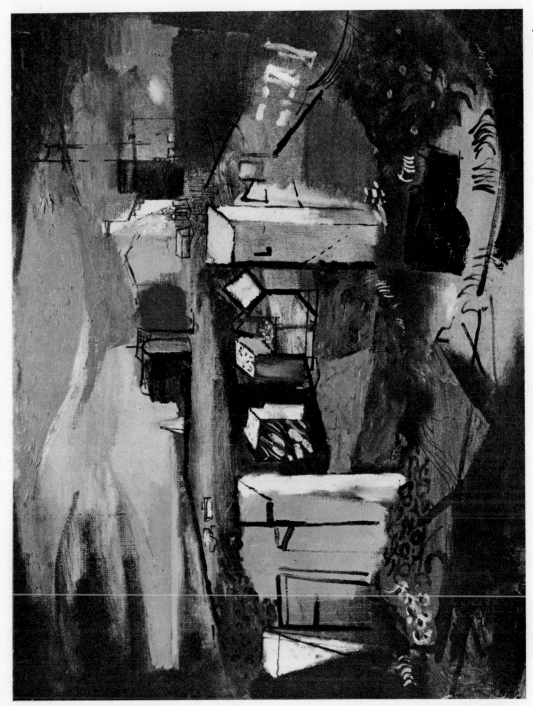

229 JOHN PIPER

Stone Gate, Portland

230 KARL ZERBE

231 GRAHAM SUTHERLAND

Vine Pergola

232a VAUGHN FLANNERY   The Governor's Cup

232b CAMERON BOOTH   Street in Stillwater

233 VACLAV VYTLACIL

Nine P.M.

After-Dinner Coffee in a City

236a LEE GATCH   Marching Highlanders

236b LEE GATCH   Industrial Night

Three Candidates for Election

238a MARK TOBEY   Marriage

238b BEN SHAHN   Still Music

239a JOHN GERNAND   Blowing Leaves

239b JOSEPH GERARD   High Tide

242 I. RICE PEREIRA   Transversion

243   NAUM GABO   Linear Construction, Variation

245 MORRIS GRAVES

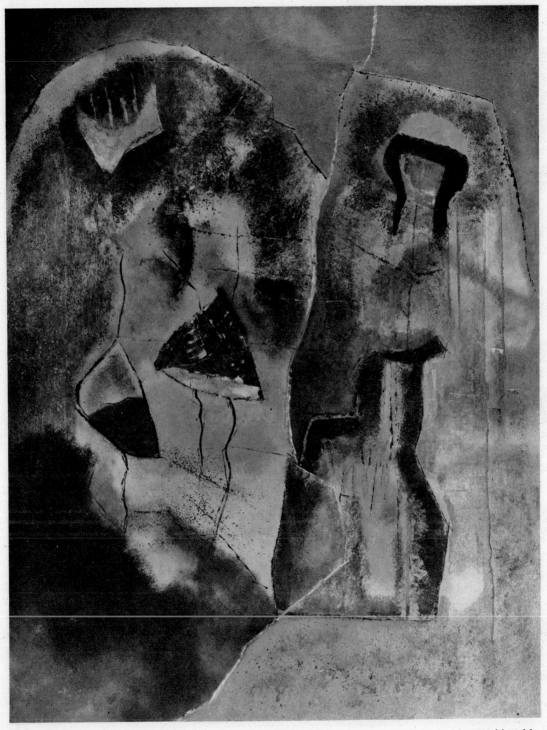

247 THEODOROS STAMOS.   World Tablet

248a HAROLD GIESE   Bananas

248b MARY B. WATKINS   The Blue and the Strawberry Roan

249 WILLIAM ZORACH   Sailing by Moonlight

250a BERNICE CROSS   Strawberry Basket

250b BERNICE CROSS   Sunken Treasure

251 BERNICE CROSS   Stone Angel

252a HERMAN MARIL   Baltimore Waterfront

252b JEAN LURÇAT   Smyrna

253 RALSTON CRAWFORD   Boat and Grain Elevators

254 ROBERT GATES   Sunflower

255a JAMES McLAUGHLIN   Anemones   255b EDWARD ROSENFELD   Kitchen Sink

257 JACOB LAWRENCE   Woman at Work ("Migration of the Negro" Series)

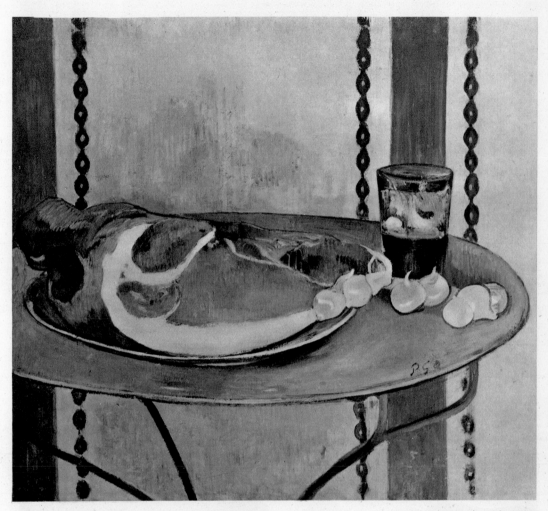

258 PAUL GAUGUIN   Still Life with Ham

259*a*   Fragment Coptic Tapestry

259*b* KEITH VAUGHAN   Yorkshire Farm House

Night Baseball

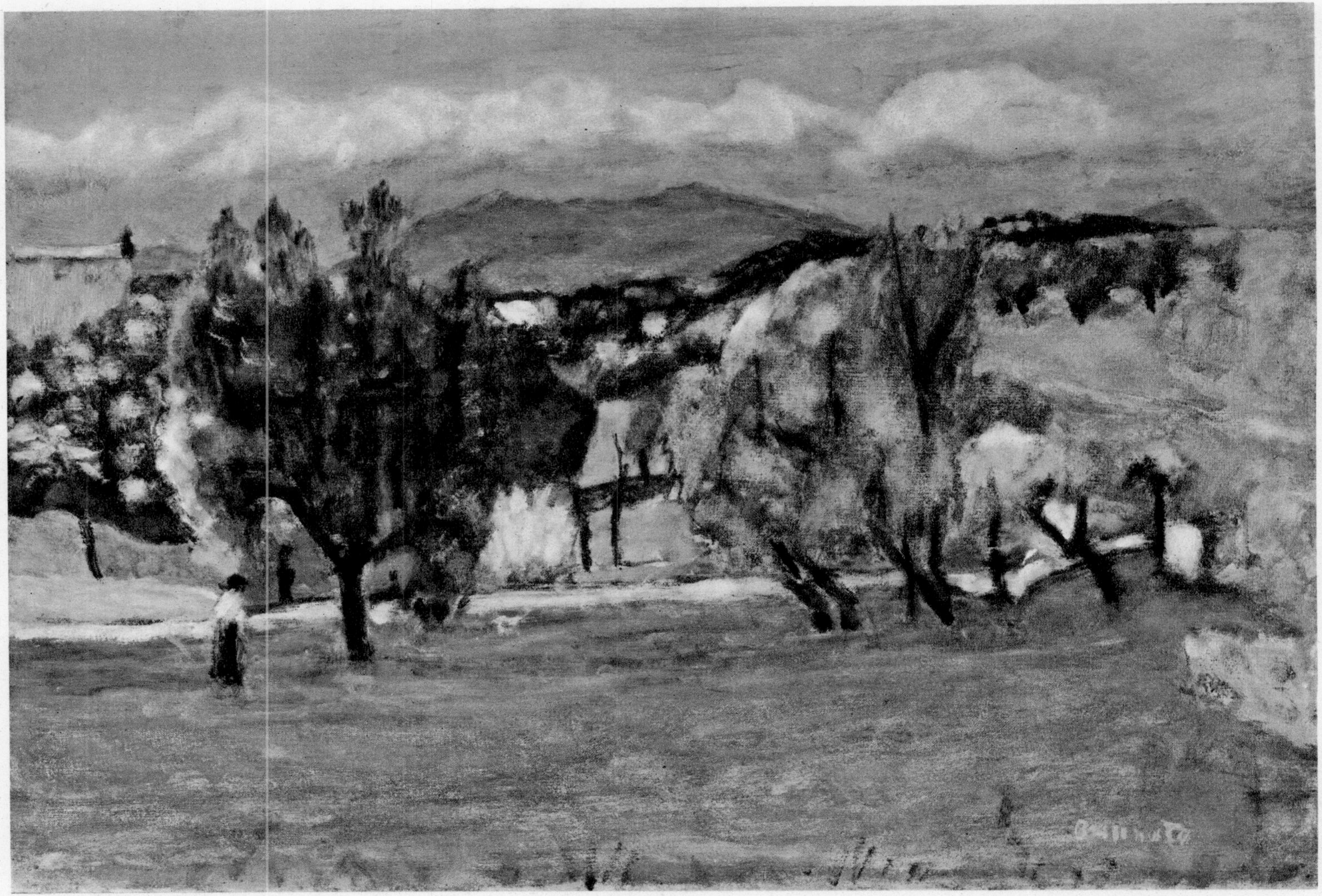

261 PIERRE BONNARD Landscape with Mountains

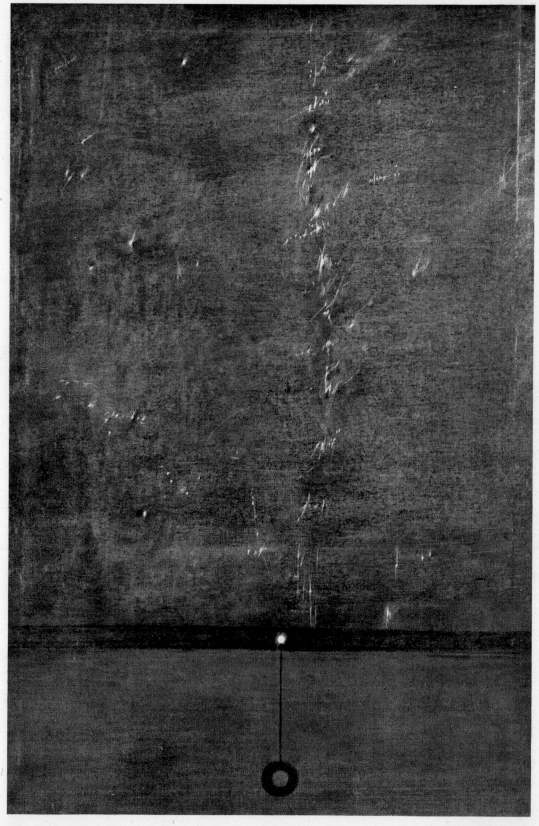

Window Shade

264 Adolph Gottlieb

INDEX

INDEX